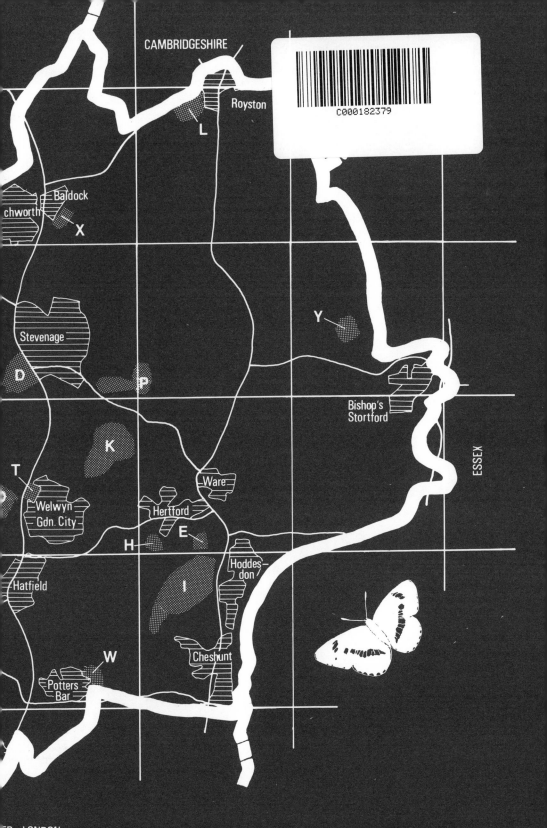

CAMBRIDGESHIRE

Royston

C000182379

L

Baldock

chworth

X

Stevenage

D

P

Y

Bishop's
Stortford

K

ESSEX

T

Ware

Welwyn
Gdn. City

Hertford

E

H

Hoddes-
don

Hatfield

I

W

Cheshunt

Potters
Bar

ER LONDON

# The Butterflies of Hertfordshire

# The Butterflies
## of
# Hertfordshire

*by*

BRIAN SAWFORD

Photographs by the Author

**CASTLEMEAD PUBLICATIONS**
WARE

First published in 1987

CASTLEMEAD PUBLICATIONS
Swains Mill, 4A Crane Mead, Ware
Herts., SG12 9PY

Publishing division of
WARD'S PUBLISHING SERVICES


ISBN 0 948555 03 3


© Brian Sawford 1987

Photographs © Brian Sawford 1987


**British Library Cataloguing in Publication Data**

Sawford, Brian
   The butterflies of Hertfordshire.
   1. Butterflies——England——
   Hertfordshire
   I. Title
   595.78′09425′8     QL555.G7
   ISBN 0-948555-03-3

Printed in Great Britain
in 10pt Century Type
by Anchor Brendon Limited, Tiptree, Essex

# Foreword

When we look at our rural landscape and the wildlife that lives within it, there are certain images and sounds which give it its unique character: a rookery in March, the sound of a Cuckoo in May, the Skylarks lifting off from downland to be pulled away by the breeze, a hazy Summer afternoon, the misty woods and mellow tones of Autumn – and of course the first butterfly of Spring.

Butterflies, throughout the Summer and early Autumn, give that extra charm to the countryside, inviting you to their secret world that can so easily pass unnoticed, but once you have discovered it it is unmistakably obvious that butterflies are an essential part of the fabric and pleasure of the countryside.

The many species of butterflies need a varied landscape, and it is this that we have lost, with a consequent decline in all species.

Brian Sawford's book is a major contribution to the knowledge of Hertfordshire's butterflies, highlighting their problems, and above all attempting to remedy the situation.

Butterflies need the countryside we all need to survive, and so in protecting the world of the butterfly, we automatically protect a varied countryside, its wildlife and a landscape worthy of future generations.

GORDON BENINGFIELD
*April 1987*

# To
# Terri

'The butterfly counts not months,
but moments, and has time enough'.

Rabindranath Tagor, *Fireflies*

# Acknowledgements

No work such as this can ever be accomplished without the help and co-operation of many people and to everyone who has contributed I am sincerely grateful. The names of some, who provided the basis of the early studies of butterflies in Hertfordshire, have been unfortunately lost with the passage of time. Many will go unmentioned in this text, but their names will remain, associated with the data they provided, in the various archives and collections that they helped to found. These and the writings of earlier Hertfordshire entomologists, especially A. E. Gibbs and Dr A. H. Foster, established a firm basis for later studies and comparisons of the county's butterflies. Particular thanks must go to all those, listed below, who collected field records during the 1984 to 1986 Hertfordshire Butterfly Atlas Project, without which this book would have been impossible. Should anyone be omitted by name I offer my apologies.

Primarily I must thank my wife, Terri, and our children for patience and understanding during my long absences from home in the production of the final text. Trevor James, my colleague in the North Hertfordshire Museums' Natural History Department at Baldock, gave a great deal of assistance in processing records and map production, and much useful, critical discussion and comment based on his own wide experience of Hertfordshire's natural history. The Hertfordshire Natural History Society, notably through the work of the Secretary, Philip Kingsbury, provided the means to initiate the Butterfly Atlas Project, and many members contributed records. Also the Society was most generous in making a grant towards the inclusion of some of the colour plates. Gordon Beningfield, despite being extremely busy on the production of a book of his own, kindly provided the foreword which emphasises the concern that we should all feel for the plight of our butterflies.

Thanks must go to North Hertfordshire District Council who, through their Museums Services, backed the establishment of a Biological Records Centre in the Natural History Department in 1975, and have supported the documentation and collation of butterfly records. Similar acknowledgement is also given to St Albans City and District Council who, through Phil Collins, Keeper of Natural History, and his Manpower Services Commission team operating the South Hertfordshire Biological Records Centre at City Museum, have supplied much field and collections data for the southern part of the county. The London Natural History Society, who ran a similar butterfly survey in the London area which included parts of Hertfordshire, is thanked for the supply of many relevant records received through its survey organiser, Colin Plant. Staff of the Biological Records Centre at Monks Wood were most helpful and allowed me extensive use of their butterfly data files. Dr John Catt kindly agreed to the publication of the geological map, with some slight amendments made by Neil Jarvis and re-drawn by staff at Hertfordshire County

Council. Dr Ken Smith allowed use of data from his *Hertfordshire Breeding Bird Atlas* and generously supplied base maps for use in the final mapping of species distribution. Thanks also go to the controlling authorities and staff of Haileybury College, Welwyn/Hatfield Museum and Bishops Stortford College, for unlimited access to their collections and archives. Glen Castle is thanked for his help with photocopying maps and manuscripts, and for many enjoyable hours in the field photographing butterflies.

To Alan Ward and all at Castlemead Publications, I, on behalf of many, offer a sincere vote of thanks for the foresight and commitment to produce a fine range of publications of local interest, which will stand the test of time, both in their usefulness as reference works and quality of production. I am especially grateful for all the help they have given me from inception to final production of this book.

Participants who carried out fieldwork and submitted records in the Hertfordshire Butterfly Atlas Project 1984 to 1986 were:

Dr N. Agar; Dr M. Aldridge; Mrs L. Alexander; Mrs A. Allen; Mrs B. M. Allen; G. E. Allington; D. Anderson; Dr J. E. Anderson; G. Annibal; Mrs Baby; Mrs M. Badham; G. Baker; J. Baker; J. B. Baker; Mrs M. Banthorpe; A. P. Bernard; M. G. Berry; A. Bolitho; D. Boyce; H. Boyer; Mrs P. Briggs and family; A. Bristow; Mrs M. Brown; F. Buckle; P. Buckle; R. Burrows; C. Burton; C. Bushell; D. Calnon; M. Campbell; G. M. Castle; M. Catt; J. Chapman; Cheshunt Natural History Society; Dr A. Clements; Mrs D. Coates; R. Cole; P. Collins; P. R. Colston; J. Copleston; J. Coupar; A. Cox; M. Crafer; D. Crawley; Mrs M. Crips; P. Cross; Mr and Mrs J. Crozier; W. Darling; M. Davies; A. Dean; D. Dench; Mrs M. Dickens; Dr J. Dickson; D. Draper; Ms F. Earle; S. E. Eaton; M. Eden; A. Epstein; J. Fielding; Flamstead J. M. I. School (Class 3); Ms C. Forbes; Dr A. M. George; M. Gerrard; M. Gittos; Rev. T. W. Gladwin; B. Goater; A. Goodrich; Ms S. Gorton; Mrs P. Grundy; Mrs B. Harold; Ms E. Harold; J. Harris; M. Harris; M. A. Harris; C. Herbert; G. Herbert; Ms M. Holden; A. Horder; Mrs C. Horton; A. C. Jackson; P. Jackson; Mrs C. M. James; Mrs O. James; T. J. James; P. Jeffery; P. Jenner; G. Jones; K. R. Jones; Ms J. Kelly; M. Kennedy; J. King; Mrs P. J. King; P. Kingsbury; M. Lamb; J. Leonhardt; B. P. Lightfoot; J. Marchant; Ms M. Mardell; Ms E. Maughan; J. Melling; Mrs L. Merrick; Mrs B. Miles; P. Monery; P. Morgan; P. G. Morgan; T. Morton; Mr Murdoch; S. Murray; M. Newland; R. Newton; P. S. Oakley; D. Owen; Mrs S. Owen; G. M. Palmer; D. Parsons; R. Payne; M. Pearson; Rev. J. Pedlar; R. Penrose; S. Pittman; M. Phillips; A. Pratt; Ms J. Pugh; G. Reed; J. Reed; J. Reid; A. M. Riley; D. Robertson; Ms K. Robinson; M. D. Russell; B. R. Sawford; D. J. Schrader; J. Scivyer; G. Scouthern; G. H. B. Sell; Ms H. Senior; Mrs C. Shepperson; J. G. Simpson; A. M. Slater; L. Smart; C. Smith; Dr K. Smith; Mrs L. Smith; D. Southworth; A. B. Spackman; B. Squires; P. Stead; A. R. Stephenson; R. Stroud; G. Swann; J. Terry; D. Thompson; Mrs V. Thorne; C. Tipper; J. Tomkins; Mrs J. Turberville; M. Tyrrell; J. Wallace; P. Walton; M. Ward; Mr and Mrs C. Watson; Mrs P. Watson; Mrs G. Webb; D. J. Wedd; G. White; I. Whitehouse; P. Whittington; B. Wildridge; S. Wilson; A. Winterford; I. Woiwod; A. Woods.

# Contents

# List of Illustrations

# List of Tables

# List of Colour Plates

# 1

# Introduction

The varied history of geological deposition, changing weather patterns and use of the land throughout Hertfordshire has created a wide range of semi-natural butterfly habitats. In the last two hundred years or so, collectors and naturalists have recorded fifty-four species of butterflies in the county. They have also witnessed marked losses and changes in species and habitats, as the deleterious effects of developing agriculture, urbanisation and other pressures have spread to virtually all parts. Although there have been some gains, usually only temporarily, reductions predominate and these are compounded by the effects of poor weather on populations reduced by the loss or degradation of habitats. Until recently little has been done properly to assess the true status of the various species or to conserve those threatened with local extinction. Almost unnoticed, a number of species have been lost and several others have been reduced to perilously low numbers.

With a realisation of some of the problems facing our butterflies, and in an attempt to remedy the situation, I, in conjunction with the Hertfordshire Natural History Society, established the Hertfordshire Butterfly Atlas Project in 1983. From 1984 to 1986 extensive fieldwork was undertaken in the county, with help from nearly two hundred members of the Society and others. The results of the survey form the basis of this book, which also brings together, for the first time, published information and a great deal of other historical data gleaned from many sources, including previously unpublished collections and notebooks. It is a sincere hope that this book will be used positively to encourage the future conservation and continued recording of our butterflies. To assist this, some basic identification and ecological requirements are included in the species accounts.

# 2

# The County of Hertford

About forty miles (64 km) from west to east, thirty-three miles (53 km) north to south and landlocked, Hertfordshire is one of England's smaller counties. It encompasses some 630 square miles (163 415 hectares) of mainly undulating but varied countryside, based upon soft, easily eroded, geological deposits. Outstanding topographical features are few and mainly confined to the escarpment of the Chalk, which forms much of the north-western boundary of the county. At 804 feet (245 m) above sea-level, Hastoe Hill near Tring, is the highest point. Away from the scarp slope the landscape is gentler. Two plateaux of higher ground stretch from Cuffley to Bushey, and from Redbourn to Hatfield. Most of the population, of just under a million, reside in the southern half of the county. Away from the conurbations much of Hertfordshire remains largely agricultural, with extensive areas of arable and improved grasslands, which are not conducive to good butterfly populations.

For the purpose of natural history recording, Hertfordshire is defined as follows – all the area within the administrative boundary established in 1965, including Potters Bar Urban District formerly in Middlesex, a small area near Holwell formerly in Bedfordshire, and those areas transferred from Hertfordshire – Barnet and East Barnet Districts to the London Borough of Barnet and parts of Hemel Hempstead Rural District to Bedfordshire. In national and local biological recording contexts this combined area is known as Watsonian Vice County 20, often abbreviated to VC 20.

# 3

# Geology, Soils and Landscape

Butterflies depend upon plants, whose distributions are largely determined by the nature of the soils produced from the variety of underlying geological deposits. Hertfordshire's geology (Figure 3.1) is
founded on sediments laid beneath the relatively shallow, warm seas
of the Cretaceous period. The earliest of these, Gault Clay and Upper
Greensand, were deposited over a hundred-million years ago, and
today form much of the low-lying country at the foot of the Chalk
escarpment. Only small outcrops are found within the county, near
Ashwell and to the north of Tring. Chalk, a soft, white limestone
principally composed of the remains of micro-fossils such as foramin-
ifera, was laid down over the Gault. Its maximum thickness in Hertfordshire is 680 feet (207 m), although much has been removed by
erosion, and extensive areas are now obscured by later deposits. On
the basis of its nature and included fossils the Chalk is divided into
three major horizons, Lower, Middle and Upper Chalk. The upper
horizons are particularly characterised by flints, which formed within
the sediments after they consolidated.

Having deposited Gault Clay and Chalk over wide areas of Europe,
the Cretaceous seas retreated about sixty-five million years ago, when
earth movements, which were finally to form the Alpine Mountains,
uplifted the Earth's crust. For nearly twenty million years the newly
created 'chalk' land enjoyed a sub-tropical climate and was eroded by
extensive river systems. About fifty million years ago, at the start of
the Eocene period, parts of eastern and southern England were again
covered by a shallow sea spreading from the east. The effects of this
were to erode the surface of the Chalk flat, and lay down over it thirty-
to-fifty-feet thick (9–15 m) deposits – the Reading Beds. These consist
of sands and clays over a basal pebble bed. In places the pebbles are
cemented with silica and iron oxide to form a hard conglomerate
known as Hertfordshire Puddingstone.

For a period the sea regressed again as further earth movements
uplifted and tilted the land. Erosion followed until a further and
deeper encroachment of the sea resulted in the deposition of up to 300
feet (91 m) of dark grey, stiff London Clay over the Reading Beds. As
the sea finally regressed at the close of the Eocene period, about forty
million years ago, beds, up to fifty feet (15 m) thick, of fine sandy clays
were laid down. These are the Claygate Beds and are the youngest of
Hertfordshire's solid deposits (not shown on the geological map).

During the thirty-five million years or so after Eocene times, erosion
removed considerable amounts of the Claygate Beds, London Clay and
Reading Beds, particularly from northern and western parts of the
county. Much of the Chalk was exposed to further erosion. Outliers of

the Reading Beds remained on some of the south-eastern slopes of the newly formed Chiltern Hills. Today, Reading Beds still cap some of the isolated hills in the south and west of the county, although they may be obscured by later superficial deposits. Earth movements which compounded the building of the Alpine mountains of southern Europe compressed Cretaceous and Eocene strata, producing lateral folding, and some faulting across south-east England. The London basin syncline was thus formed, with its northern limb across Hertfordshire, dipping to the south-east.

Clay-with-Flints, a reddish brown clay with abundant Reading Beds pebbles and flints from the Upper Chalk, covers much of the Upper Chalk of the south-west. It is thought to have developed when thin deposits of the Reading Beds were weathered and disturbed. At the same time the surface of the Upper Chalk was dissolved, leaving spaces around the insoluble flints which were filled with clay from above or deposited from water circulating through the strata. These processes which formed the Clay-with-Flints probably started in the Eocene.

From about one-and-a-half million years ago a steadily deteriorating global climate reached its nadir in the Ice Ages of the Pleistocene period. Most of the superficial deposits were laid down during this period of rapidly fluctuating climate, which ranged from arctic to warm temperate. Glacial episodes of up to 100,000 years' duration were responsible for much erosion and, particularly, the great accumulations of superficial deposits which produced the variety of soil types of Hertfordshire. These glacials were separated by shorter interglacials when the climate was frequently much warmer than today. The nature of these stages has been determined by close examination of deposits, erosion features and fossil assemblages. Pollen remains preserved in contemporary peat and lake sediments have been particularly important in determination of climate and vegetational changes.

In the four most recent glacials, ice sheets spread into lowland Britain from montane areas of Wales, Scotland and Scandinavia. Only in the first two of these (the Beestonian and Anglian) did ice actually reach Hertfordshire. It is estimated that, at times, the moving ice sheets and glaciers may have been up to a kilometre thick. Vast amounts of bedrock were crushed, eroded and transported away by the ice, to create much of the topography we see today. The steep escarpment running south-west to north-east along much of the western margin of the county testifies to this. When climatic conditions ameliorated, meltwaters caused further erosion. In many places the ice-created topography became buried as deposits accumulated from meltwaters, and moraine were left by the retreating ice.

As glaciers and ice sheets move, their undersurfaces rasp over the rocks, grinding them up into fine clays, called *tills*. Larger fragments, often of more obdurate rocks, termed *erratics*, may be plucked off and transported with the tills. Such glacial erratics are very useful in studies of the origins and directions of movement of the glaciers. When the ice melted tills were deposited over a wide area. The Chiltern Drift, found in a narrow belt south of St Albans, and the Pebbly Clay

Drift of parts of south-east Herfordshire, date from the effects of several glaciations, the first of which occurred about 500 000 years ago. Chalky Boulder Clay, a till containing abundant Chalk erratics, covers large areas of the north and east of the county, with outliers near St Albans and in the south-east. This resulted from the Anglian glaciation of some 300 000 years ago. At that time ice from north-eastern Britain covered much of East Anglia, reaching the Chalk escarpment, with lobes penetrating the Vale of St Albans and as far as North London. It is probable that Anglian glaciers only topped and eroded the Chalk escarpment north of a line from Lilley to Whitwell, reducing its height and removing the Clay-with-Flints.

Waters flowing out from the glaciers as they advanced and retreated laid down great quantities of sands and gravels across Hertfordshire, producing a complex series of deposits, especially in the river valleys of the south and east. This situation was further complicated when Anglian ice in the Vale of St Albans blocked the proto-River Thames. Its course, north-eastwards through Hertfordshire, to reach the North Sea off Suffolk, was diverted eastwards through what is now London. Gravel terraces of the proto-Thames form significant deposits sweeping across the south of the county. Some of the Pebble Gravels, related to the proto-Thames and its north-flowing tributary, the proto-River Mole, are almost certainly of pre-Beestonian age and, with the exception of some parts of the Clay-with-Flints, are the oldest superficial deposits found in Hertfordshire.

Although Hertfordshire remained unglaciated during the last two cold stages (the Wolstonian and Devensian), periglacial conditions persisted. Permafrost and summer thaws caused instability in both solid and superficial deposits. With no protective vegetation to speak of, soils were washed or slid down slopes to accumulate as solifluction deposits, notably on the steep-sided hills of the Chalk escarpment. Upper surfaces and thinner deposits of Boulder Clay were, and still are, affected by decalcification and solifluction to form argillic brown earth soils. Cold winds from the north and east blew large amounts of silt (*loess*) over the landscape. Much of this is incorporated within the solifluction deposits. Thin patches occur throughout the county, although a good deal has been removed by more recent drainage and redeposited by rivers. In some places these River Brickearths are quite substantial, as at Hitchin, Hertford, Cheshunt and Rickmansworth. In the last 10 000 years the only significant deposits to accumulate have been alluvium along the courses of the rivers. Forest clearance and agricultural activities, following the Neolithic occupation of Hertfordshire about 5000 years ago, have accelerated this and the build-up of earthy deposits (*colluvium*) on lower valley slopes.

Weathering of the varied geological deposits has produced a diversity of soil types in Hertfordshire, ranging from the highly calcareous rendzinas of the Chalk escarpment to the acid podzols found on the Pebbly Clay Drift. Within these extremes are many more neutral types, whose characteristics are largely related to the availability of ground water. Soils still very much govern the distributions of many plants and consequently those animals, particularly butterflies, which depend upon them, even though the nature of Hertfordshire's vegetation has been greatly modified over the last 5000 years.

During the last glaciation the landscape would have been rather bleak with a tundra-like vegetation. As conditions improved, grasses, low scrub and finally mixed deciduous forest clothed the land. The precise nature and full extent of these prehistoric forests are still subject to detailed research. They were probably quite extensive and dense, with the possible exceptions of the chalkhills, which are thought to have supported rather light open forest, and the river valleys, where marshes and open grasslands were maintained by herds of grazing animals. In the centuries of human occupation since Neolithic times, forest clearance, grazing by domesticated stock, drainage, cultivation, urbanisation and industrialisation have eradicated the truly natural habitats of Hertfordshire. Only a few semi-natural sites, mainly woodlands, remain to give some indication of what has been lost.

Today's landscape is very much an artifact of human history, with large areas dominated by buildings and open arable lands. Yet there still remain some corners of the county, also formed by human hand, with ancient woodlands, hedges, fields, lanes and trackways where wildlife still abounds. Throughout history, wildlife, especially many of our butterflies, invaded and flourished in newly created and managed habitats, notably coppiced woods, grazed Chalk downs, heaths, commons and meadows. Many species are now restricted to those habitat types which were stable for a very long time and, because of this, are declining as stability through traditional management is

Figure 3.1  *Map showing the surface geology of the County of Hertfordshire*

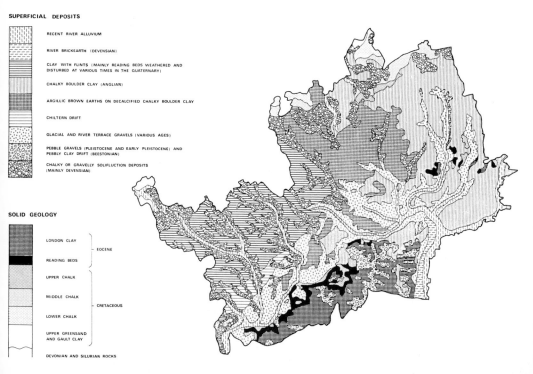

SUPERFICIAL DEPOSITS

RECENT RIVER ALLUVIUM

RIVER BRICKEARTH (DEVENSIAN)

CLAY WITH FLINTS (MAINLY READING BEDS WEATHERED AND DISTURBED AT VARIOUS TIMES IN THE QUATERNARY)

CHALKY BOULDER CLAY (ANGLIAN)

ARGILLIC BROWN EARTHS ON DECALCIFIED CHALKY BOULDER CLAY

CHILTERN DRIFT

GLACIAL AND RIVER TERRACE GRAVELS (VARIOUS AGES)

PEBBLE GRAVELS (PLEISTOCENE AND EARLY PLEISTOCENE) AND PEBBLY CLAY DRIFT (BEESTONIAN)

CHALKY OR GRAVELLY SOLIFLUCTION DEPOSITS (MAINLY DEVENSIAN)

SOLID GEOLOGY

LONDON CLAY
— EOCENE
READING BEDS

UPPER CHALK

MIDDLE CHALK
— CRETACEOUS
LOWER CHALK

UPPER GREENSAND AND GAULT CLAY

DEVONIAN AND SILURIAN ROCKS

*(Top)* Figure 3.2 *Over sixty per cent of Hertfordshire is under some form of arable cultivation. Many areas leave little room for wildlife. (Deadman's Hill, Sandon)*

*(Below)* Figure 3.3 *Rich Chalk downlands were the result of centuries of grazing by Sheep. (Coombe Bottom, near Therfield)*

removed or habitats are destroyed. In the last two centuries much of the ancient mozaic of countryside has disappeared. The human population has increased, with consequent rapid growth and changes in agriculture and industry. Much of the former way of life and use of the countryside has radically changed to the detriment of its wildlife; and this loss is typified by the declines and extinctions of several species of butterflies.

Hertfordshire County Council's Analysis of Land Use Allocation, carried out in 1982, showed that 64 per cent of the county was being farmed. Eighty per cent of this farmland was under arable cultivation, the majority of the remainder being improved grassland, that is, grassland that has been subjected to reseeding, drainage, treatment with herbicides and fertilisers, or a combination of these. About 20 per cent of the land was allocated to urban and industrial useage. What is left contains rivers, streams, canals, lakes, reservoirs, ponds, parks, commons, unimproved grasslands, scrub and woodlands. About 7 per cent of the county is wooded, but a high proportion consists of relatively recent conifer plantation, although some major areas of semi-natural woodland remain in the west and south. Many of the formerly extensive coppiced woods are now unmanaged and are losing important aspects of their wildlife interest. Large tracts of the traditionally open commons and downs of the south and west of the county have been left ungrazed for so long that shrubs and trees have almost obliterated them and to all intents they may now be regarded as woodlands.

It is estimated that less than 5 per cent of Hertfordshire retains important semi-natural habitats of wildlife interest. Most of these have been isolated or fragmented for a long time. For at least a century, naturalists have noted and bemoaned these losses which, in conjunction with changing weather patterns, have seriously affected butterfly populations. Several species, unable to cross the barriers of inhospitable landscape, were reduced to unviable populations and succumbed to periods of poor weather.

# 4

# Climate

Hertfordshire's weather, like that of the rest of Britain, is predominantly westerly in origin, but, because of the proximity of the European landmass, is subject, at times, to considerable variation from the normal relatively warm and moist conditions. Butterflies need sunshine and the amount that any habitat receives through the year has an important influence on the distribution of many species. Fewer species occur in Britain than in neighbouring Europe. Hertfordshire lacks a number of the warmth-loving species found in more southerly counties. The species distribution maps for the county show that many species have a distinct bias to the south-west, where the local climate is warmer and more humid.

In the species accounts details will be given illustrating the changes and extinctions of butterfly populations related to a general lack of sunshine. This may occur from prolonged poor summers or because habitats have become overgrown or shady, particularly inhibiting egg and larval development. Fine, sunny, warm summers and harsh, but not prolonged, winters promote population increases, but long summer droughts and mild, damp winters usually cause declines. Each species has its own characteristics and tolerances to extremes.

From about 1800 there was a general rise in overall temperature and rainfall in Britain. This lasted until the 1870s, when significant declines in annual mean temperatures and decreasing south-westerly winds were experienced, possibly associated with a southerly shift in pressure belts. Other hypotheses have been put forward to explain the reduction in temperature; suggested contributing factors include the approximate 11- or 22-year cycle of sunspot activity and atmospheric pollution. Emissions from distant volcanic eruptions scatter vast quantities of material into the upper atmosphere; for two or three years after the great eruptions of 1883, 1885, 1902 and 1912 monthly solar radiation was reduced by over twenty per cent. Atmospheric pollution was also increased by the uncontrolled wastes of the industrial revolution; there have been recent suggestions linking atmospheric sulphur dioxide pollution and acid rain to butterfly declines.

By the early 1900s recorders were noting butterfly declines resulting from poor weather. Further losses occurred as habitats were neglected or destroyed to meet the exigences of the First World War. By the 1930s winds and pressure belts shifted northward to bring noticeably warmer weather to the British Isles. This coincided with the agricultural depression and social upheavals of the period and resulted in quite notable increases in many butterflies. In the 1940s pressure belts drifted back southwards, with a fall in mean winter temperatures. Several very good butterfly years were recorded during that decade. The years 1945 and 1947 were exceptional, producing some very early emergences and late broods.

During the 1950s spring and summer mean temperatures were lowered. Again butterflies decreased, but probably more dramatically than ever before, because of the scale of habitat loss which was exacerbated by wartime ploughing, timber felling and reduction of marginal areas. Of particular importance to butterflies was the almost complete eradication of Rabbits through myxomatosis, which swept the country in 1954 and subsequent years. Nearly all the remaining grasslands and woods became too overgrown and shady for many of the rarer species and they suffered accordingly. There have been suggestions that an increase in Hedgehogs, eating more larvae, may have effected some further reductions and, possibly, an increase in the rearing of game birds could have produced similar repercussions. Some decreases in solar radiation are probable at this time from atmospheric pollution related to dust from nuclear explosions, water vapour and gases from high flying aircraft.

More recently there has been a greater variability of climate, with more extremes. Summers of the 1960s were erratic, but generally cool and wet, with declines in many butterflies. Throughout the 1970s spring temperatures remained low, although there was a decrease in the amount of spring and summer rainfall. The great drought of 1976 severely reduced many species. Grassland 'browns', Small Heath, most 'blues' and Small Copper were seriously reduced in numbers as the foodplants of their larvae became desiccated, and it took several years for some populations to recover. Facilitated by the warmer summers, Marbled White, Speckled Wood and White Admiral started to gain ground in the late 1970s and, to date, have continued slowly to re-occupy much of their former territories. In the present decade the trend has been towards colder, wetter, later springs, variable summers and winters, and longer autumns. Results from the 1984 to 1986 Survey will provide a good basis for the future monitoring of butterfly populations, especially with regard to climatic changes.

# 5

# Hertfordshire's Major Butterfly Habitats

About a quarter of the fifty-four species of butterfly recorded in Hertfordshire are still well distributed throughout the county and can be found in a variety of habitats. Many of the other resident species are more or very restricted in their distributions because of their reliance upon specialised habitats or the scarcity of larval foodplants. Seven species (excluding vagrants) have become extinct since records began over 200 years ago. Wood White and Large Tortoiseshell, former residents, now only occur as vagrants. Several species have significantly declined and, although a few have increased, this emphasises some of the radical changes that have taken place in our countryside. Particularly evident is the extensive loss of ancient woodlands and grasslands where destruction and cessation of traditional management have been most effective in reducing or eliminating populations of the more specialised butterflies.

## 5.1 Woodlands

There is little doubt that from about 11 000 B.C., when the last glaciation ended, to 5000 B.C., most of Hertfordshire was extensively covered with forest, or wildwood. Small-leaved Lime, or Pry and Hazel were probably the dominant trees, with oaks and elms well represented. On the southern plateaus with the acid soils birches, Hornbeam, Rowan, Aspen, Yew and Holly would have been frequent. Steep slopes on the Chalk were clothed with a mixture of Ash, Wych Elm, Yew, Field Maple and Cherry, with a rich variety of calcicolous shrubs including Whitebeam, Sallow and Juniper, to form a rather more open type of forest. Beech was present, but only as a relatively minor component. Today's extensive Chiltern beechwoods derive mainly from nineteenth century plantings to supply the needs of the furniture trade. Structurally the wildwood was very different from the woods we see in Hertfordshire now and it was probably full of forest butterflies such as Purple Emperor, White Admiral, Wood White, woodland fritillaries and hairstreaks.

Around 5000 B.C. Neolithic settlers began to clear the wildwood to make way for crops and grazing animals. Within the next two millenia much of the wildwood had been removed. Domesticated sheep and goats turned out into the cleared areas were most effective in preventing the regeneration of shrubs and trees, their grazings benefiting the development of low growing herbs and grasses to produce new semi-natural grasslands. This opening up of the landscape facilitated the spread of many non-woodland butterflies.

Most historical ecologists now consider that by Roman times most, if not all, of Hertfordshire's chalklands had been cleared of forest to produce vast tracts of grasslands or sheepwalks, with scattered, small arable fields, especially on the deeper soils in valleys and along the base of the escarpment. The rest of the county was a patchwork of farmland, woodland and small settlements, with probably some more extensive woods remaining on poorer and less easily cultivated soils. Already most of the characteristics of the wildwood had been changed. Where woods did occur they became part of the local economy with grazing or browsing domestic stock, or, more importantly, they were subjected to long-term woodland practices of cultivation, selective felling and coppicing. Management techniques practised and refined over many centuries were employed in many of our woods until the present century.

Since at least Neolithic times some areas of land were used for the dual purposes of wood production and livestock grazing. These wood pastures remained, until the eighteenth or early nineteenth century, as quite large areas in the southern part of Hertfordshire. They were frequently characterised by their ancient trees, pollarded to keep the foliage out of the reach of cattle and horses. Many of the now wooded commons were formerly wood pasture that reverted when grazing was withdrawn. Typical examples are parts of Northaw Great Wood, Broxbourne Woods, Ashridge, Hitch and Knebworth Woods. Wood pastures benefited those butterflies which require mosaics of sheltered habitats such as fritillaries, Grizzled and Dingy Skippers.

Until the nineteenth century coppicing-with-standards remained a most significant form of woodland management in Hertfordshire. This involved cutting blocks of underwood or shrubs on a regular cycle (of about fourteen years' duration, although later this was generally

Figure 5.1 *Many former wood pastures and commons have now become overgrown with trees. (Hitch Wood)*

extended). Standard trees were left and felled for timber when mature or as required. Coppiced materials were utilised for many purposes including firewood (much of the county's hornbeam fuelled the fires of London), hurdle construction, fences and poles. The selectiveness of regional requirements, coupled with the varying soils, determined the productivity of the various trees and shrubs and what would be allowed to grow – factors which are largely responsible for the nature of the different types of woodland that survive today. Regular and long-term coppicing had a profound effect upon the woodland micro-climate and ground flora, which favoured certain butterflies, notably the woodland fritillaries. Once the widespread practice ceased these species declined rapidly.

Throughout the Dark Ages and Anglo-Saxon periods the landscape of Hertfordshire was probably managed more or less as in Roman times. A few areas perhaps reverted to woodland. Rackham (1986) estimates that about 30 per cent of the county was wooded at the time of the Domesday Book in 1086, most of which was confined to the south. By this time most of the woods had been so managed that they probably already fell into one or more of the eighteen main stand types now recognised. Of the major stand types Sessile Oak predominates on sandy and lighter loam soils, whilst Pedunculate Oak is most common on heavy clays. Oak-with-Hornbeam occupies much of the south and south-east, and Ash-with-Maple is most frequent on the Boulder Clay of the north-east. As noted above, Beech woods of the Chalk escarpment were a later addition to the landscape.

During the 13th and 14th centuries pressures of population increase and consequent hunger for land in England resulted in great woodland clearances, as Rackham (1986) emphasises 'reducing the woods to something like their present extent by 1350'. Although the Black Death of 1349 halted this onslaught there was probably little reversion and many of our primary woods, derived from the wildwood, were present at this time with well defined boundaries. Secondary woods, which have developed naturally on land that was not previously wooded, may be of any age, from prehistoric to most recent. These are often dominated by oaks, birches, Ash and Common Hawthorn which readily invade vacant ground. Ground flora of these secondary woods is usually less diverse than that of primary woods and insect populations are significantly less varied.

Plantations abound in the county and usually comprise of one or two species of non-natural trees, often conifers. They are generally of relatively recent origin. Frequently entire or parts of ancient woods are replaced with plantations which, unlike primary or secondary woods, do not normally maintain themselves when cut. They have to be replanted. Ground flora of plantations, particularly where conifers are grown, is usually impoverished by shading and acidification of the soil, and of little importance to butterflies once the tree canopy has closed, although some rides and margins can produce good sheltered habitats, as can failed plantations.

For centuries the majority of woods and wood pastures remained stable in a countryside of interlinking trackways, lanes, hedges and

13

Figure 5.2 *Wide rides and open areas in both deciduous and conifer woods will support a wide variety of butterflies. (Broxbourne Woods)*

meadows. Their cheap and renewable resources were realised and maintained, for example coppices were cut in blocks, or coupes, so that in any year there would be freshly cut areas, developing coppice and material ready for cutting in the following years. Such management favoured many forms of wildlife, the freshly cut coppices soon developed a rich ground flora that suited the breeding requirements of fritillaries, Dingy and Grizzled Skippers and Small Copper. Thirty-seven species of butterfly have been recorded from the woodlands of Hertfordshire, and of these only White-letter and Purple Hairstreaks are entirely dependant upon trees, the remainder relying upon suitably managed shrubs and ground flora for breeding. Many of these butterflies declined as coppicing regimes lengthened and ceased; three species of fritillary have become extinct and several other species are now down to levels which give great concern for their future in the county.

Various economic and social changes have affected the status and quality of woodlands in the last two centuries. The coming of the railways made coal a cheaper fuel than coppice. Although short-lived, the agricultural boom of the mid-19th century led to the loss of some ancient woods. New fashions saw many landowners establishing or replanting woods with conifers and alien hardwoods (Sycamore, hybrid limes and Rhododendron). Often woods and copses were retained for the sole purpose of raising game birds. Much timber was felled during the two World Wars. The intervening years of depression saw great changes in land tenure, with some clearances to provide ready capital.

About 7 per cent of Hertfordshire is still wooded, and of this 7 per cent only 2 per cent is ancient broad-leaved wood and is very fragmented throughout the county. Oak with old Hornbeam coppice is most widespread, with good examples at Northaw Great Wood, Balls, Wormley, Hoddesdon Park, Sherrardspark, Whippendell and Bricket Woods. Oxhey Woods and Northaw Great Wood have good stands of Oak-with-Birch and there are fine Beech plantations in the Ashridge area. Boulder Clay woods are now largely isolated amongst arable lands with some of the best examples of Ash-with-Maple at Great Hormead Park and Northey Wood. Examination of the distribution map of the Purple Hairstreak gives a fair indication of the distribution of extant ancient semi-natural woodlands in Hertfordshire.

Because of the deterioration and destruction of our woods many formerly typical butterflies have been lost. Several of these are species which require relatively large areas to maintain viable populations. Such areas must contain suitable breeding habitat as well as adult feeding sites, for example flowery rides, lanes and meadows, features now missing from much of the Hertfordshire landscape. In recent years, mainly from the instigation of conservation bodies, there has been some return to small scale coppicing. It is unlikely that species such as the woodland fritillaries will return unless reintroduced. White Admiral, Comma and Speckled Wood have re-occupied some of their former strongholds, but their ecological requirements are rather different and they, apparently, more readily cross large areas of inhospitable countryside to reach isolated woods.

## 5.2   Grasslands

From very early times large tracts of grassland were created from the clearances of the wildwood. Centuries of grazing and cutting produced different types of sward, which mainly related to the nature of the underlying soils. Populations of plants and animals formerly restricted to woodland clearings, flood plains, cliffs and screes quite rapidly occupied these new semi-natural habitats. Of the thirty-four species of butterflies recorded from Hertfordshire's grasslands, twenty were, or are, directly dependant upon them. Several, restricted to the more specialised types of grassland, are now scarce, and Silver-spotted Skipper, Adonis Blue, Marsh Fritillary and Grayling are extinct.

In the past 200 years, and certainly during this century, very significant reductions in both the extent and quality of our grasslands have occurred, as intensive arable cultivation has replaced pastoral farming. Much was ploughed and most of the remainder has been improved by draining, reseeding, fertiliser applications and treatment with herbicides. These have eliminated many of the native grasses and herbs and reduced butterfly populations. Unimproved flowery grasslands have almost disappeared from Hertfordshire's countryside. The breakdown of common rights at the turn of the century exacerbated this and many large areas lost their grazing animals. They soon became rank and overgrown with shrubs and trees, and were finally rendered unsuitable for grassland butterflies when Rabbits were wiped out by myxomatosis in the 1950s.

Richest sites for grassland butterflies are on south-facing slopes of the Chalk downs, where a diverse flora and unusually warm microclimates are found. For perhaps five millenia, Sheep and latterly Rabbits grazed much of the Chalk escarpment from Tring to Royston. On the nutrient-poor soils their close cropping was responsible for the development and maintenance of a short sward renowned for its richness of low growing herbs and fine-leaved grasses. On the mobile soils of the steeper slopes many bare patches provided basking areas for butterflies. The floral diversity attracted a wide range of insects, and many species were very specialised to survive in the short turf. Adonis, Small and Chalkhill Blues and Silver-spotted Skipper are reliant upon larval foodplants and micro-habitats that are strictly limited to limestone grasslands. Several other species have their main populations centred upon the downs.

Withdrawal of grazing allows certain, more vigorous, coarse grasses and shrubs to flourish and shade out fine-leaved grasses and herbs. Consequently the more specialised butterfly species disappeared, to be replaced by those more tolerant of taller grasses and shade, such as the browns and common skippers. These in turn are reduced if thick scrub develops. Many hundreds of acres of Chalk downland had gone under the plough by the turn of the century, only the steeper slopes surviving the advent of mechanised agriculture and the expansion of arable cultivation. By the 1930s the little open downland that remained was in isolated sites at Tring Park, Aldbury Nowers, between Hexton and Hitchin, at Weston Hills, Baldock, and Therfield Heath near Royston. Further losses occurred through ploughing in the Second World War, including the destruction of Lilley Hoo, the county's only remaining example of chalk heath. The loss of Rabbit grazing in the 1950s was particularly effective in allowing the over-growth of many sites which, coupled with the poor summers of the 1960s, resulted in the extinctions of Adonis Blue and Silver-spotted Skipper and quite serious reductions in several other species. Research carried out by the Natural History Department of North Hertfordshire

Figure 5.3 *Nearly all the ancient meadows have been lost from Hertfordshire. (Goldings Meadow near Hertford)*

Figure 5.4  *The largest remaining tract of Chalk grassland is at Therfield Heath*

Museums shows that in 1940 there were about 500 acres of good downland between Hexton and Royston. In 1984 this had been reduced to just seventy acres, most of which was within the Therfield Heath Nature Reserve. Only one site, in private hands, was still grazed by Sheep. The situation is much the same, possibly worse, on the downs in the south-west of the county. It seems likely that Small and Chalk-hill Blues, Duke of Burgundy Fritillary, Dark-green Fritillary, Dingy and Grizzled Skippers may soon be faced with local extinction unless some remedial efforts are made to safeguard the chalk grasslands.

Other types of grassland, formerly widespread in Hertfordshire, have gone or been improved and much of their wildlife interest lost. In north Hertfordshire over 90 per cent of the unimproved neutral pastures present in 1940, which had a rich flora and fauna, had been removed by 1984. This is probably typical of the county as a whole. Some of the better examples are now only found as small sites in the river valleys of the Lea, Mimram, Chess and Stort, with a few on poorly drained soils near Ardeley, Sandon, Langley and Purwell near Hitchin. Heathy acid grasslands, which used to occur frequently in south and east Hertfordshire, are now few, rather small and isolated at such sites as Hertford Heath, parts of Croxley Common Moor, Burleigh Meadow near Knebworth and Patmore Heath, Albury. Dry heathy commons still exist in west and central Hertfordshire, with examples near Berkhamsted, Chorleywood, Colney Heath and Wheat-hampstead, although substantial portions of these have become covered with scrub, planted with trees or used for recreation.

Many butterflies have been affected by the reductions of unimproved grasslands; even the common skippers and browns, which may still appear to be abundant in places, are now less numerous and face future declines. More noticeable losses have been documented for species such as Dingy and Grizzled Skippers, Common Blue, Small Copper, Wall and Ringlet. It is regrettable that today we have to regard certain road verges, railway embankments, woodland rides, edges of playing fields, churchyards and abandoned quarries as some of the better sites for grassland butterflies. Local authorities and conservation organisations must be urged to safeguard, improve and suitably manage the few important unimproved grasslands which remain in the county.

## 5.3  Hedges, Road Verges and Railway Tracks

These are becoming increasingly important for butterflies and, in today's largely unsuitable countryside, often provide the only places for breeding and feeding. Although narrow linear habitats they are frequently all that remains of former woods or grasslands in otherwise arable or urban 'deserts'. Brimstone, Orange Tip, Green-veined White, Holly Blue, Comma, Peacock and Small Tortoiseshell are some of the woodland-edge species that benefit from their ability to breed along hedgerows. Removal and neglect of the county's hedges continue to affect such species and inhibit the spread of others by removing sheltered cross-country dispersal routes and feeding sites. In central Hertfordshire, about 40 per cent of the hedges have been removed in the last thirty years.

Narrow, heavily cut road verges are not suitable for butterflies, especially where toxic sprays are used on adjacent fields. Wider, flowery verges and tracksides may, if suitably cut or grazed and protected by a good hedge, support many species, including Meadow Brown, Gatekeeper, Small Heath, Small Copper, Common Blue, Large, Small and Essex Skippers. Some of the county's relatively new trunk roads have developed verges with good butterfly populations, notably where they pass through cuttings or have wide embankments. In certain places attempts are being made to seed new verges with selected native flora. This should encourage butterflies if future management precludes the natural succession of coarse grasses and scrub. The future of all verges as butterfly habitats depends very much upon the frequency and timing of cutting regimes. In view of the

Figure 5.5  *Verges are important for butterflies but, unless managed, will soon become overgrown. (Near Baldock)*

declining status of most species more emphasis should be paid to the importance of verges and adequate consideration given to their correct management.

Since the demise of steam trains, railway tracks have lost much of their butterfly interest. Embankments and cuttings used to be kept free of coarse grasses and scrub as errant cinders caused frequent summer fires, and Rabbits forming large colonies along many lines were also of importance in maintaining an open sward. With the disappearance of both steam locomotives and Rabbits, few lengths of track retained much interest and those that did are continuing to degrade. Small Blue used to be a fairly frequent species of railway banks on the Chalk in the central and northern part of the county: it is now confined in very small numbers to just two small sites near Hitchin. Twenty-three species were recorded from a stretch of disused line running north from Ickleford to the county border with Bedfordshire, including Holly and Small Blues, Brown Argus and Speckled Wood. Despite vigorous informed opposition most of the site has been destroyed: in a few short months domestic refuse was dumped to fill the cutting and the surface was then levelled with topsoil. A short distance to the south of this a fine chalk embankment was completely cleared, reseeded and planted as a 'conservation' area: none of the rarer butterflies survived. Another disused line near Wheathampstead, the Ayot Way, is used for recreation and attracts many visitors with an interest in natural history: it too is in danger of losing some of its more interesting butterflies as coarse grasses and scrub encroach on the margins.

## 5.4 Urban

Most gardens, playing fields and waste areas are attractive to at least a few of our more mobile butterflies. Some parks, churchyards and greens have become important havens for several species. Large and Small Whites, whose larvae infest cultivated brassicas, are, perhaps, not appreciated. Others, however, are welcomed and can, with suitable planning, be encouraged to visit our towns and gardens in greater numbers, not just to feed on showy flowers but also to breed. With such a changed countryside there is an added emphasis upon the creation, use and maintenance of such areas for the conservation and aesthetic attraction of even relatively common butterflies.

Many churchyards and village greens have relic patches of unimproved grassland which, if left unmown through the summer months can produce an attractive succession of butterflies. There are many currently heavily managed playing fields and school grounds which could, at least in parts, be made similarly interesting with suitably sympathetic management and judicious planting.

Parks and, particularly, gardens can be improved for many butterflies by the growing of favourite nectar plants. It is rather more difficult to provide suitable breeding conditions. Leaving patches of taller grasses and nettles in sunny sheltered situations is worth trying and should attract species such as Gatekeeper, Meadow Brown, Small

Figure 5.6 *Small patches of grassland, relics of formerly widespread habitats, remain in some churchyards and on village greens. (Little Hormead)*

and Large Skipper, Small Tortoiseshell, Peacock and Small Heath. Three very useful guides detailing the creation and establishment of suitable butterfly habitats have been produced by Rothschild and Farrel (1983), Oates (1985) and Killingbeck (1985).

# 6

# The Historical Study of Hertfordshire's Butterflies

Between 1702 and 1709 James Petiver, one the earliest butterfly collectors or, as they were known in those times, *Aurelians*, published a work entitled *Gazophyllacii Naturae et Artis*. This contained two illustrations of a butterfly which Petiver named 'The Enfield Eye'. In 1717 Petiver published another work, which was the first to be devoted to British butterflies. Illustrated with hand-coloured woodcuts this important book bore the imposing title *Papilionum Britanniae Icones, Nomina, etc. Containing the figures, names, places, seasons, etc., of about eighty British Butter-flies, being all that have hitherto been observed in Great Britain*. This repeated the illustrations of 'The Enfield Eye' depicted in the earlier work. Figure 5 in the *Papilionum Britanniae* bears a caption showing that it was drawn from a specimen captured and named by Petiver. He explains his naming as follows, 'It [Enfield] being the place I first observed them in. These appear from April to July'. Figure 6 illustrates the other specimen and is captioned 'Idem, obscurior et serotinus [the same, darker and appearing later in the season] – The Brown Enfield Eye. Mr Dandridge first observed this about Watford, towards the end of July'. This is the first known butterfly record for Hertfordshire.

In the early days of collecting the vernacular names were often quite different than those used today. Some alluded to places where first specimens were taken or to favourite collecting grounds, others commemorated certain collectors. Both collectors and authors found difficulties in naming variations and aberrations. Often the two sexes of a species were described under different names. Much of the early literature became perplexing and confused: for example, the eighty or so forms described by Petiver in the *Papilionum Britanniae* have been trimmed down by later workers to forty-eight species. Such problems with nomenclature only began to be resolved from the mid-18th century, after the publication of the tenth edition of Linnaeus's *Systema Naturae* (*see* Chapter 9) and *The Aurelian* by Moses Harris. Standardisation of both vernacular and scientific nomenclature followed, and both 'The Enfield Eye' and 'The Brown Enfield Eye' were renamed as Speckled Wood. Petiver's specimens were probably female and male respectively.

It is quite conceivable that other 18th century, or earlier, records may yet be found for Hertfordshire, and, perhaps, even locally obtained specimens. Many of the Aurelians, pioneer entomological groups and societies, resided in or near London. It would seem likely that some of their field excursions might easily have encompassed at least parts of southern Hertfordshire. Petiver regularly travelled from his home at Aldersgate to Enfield Chase, in the old county of Middlesex, which abutted on the Hertfordshire border. Before it was dischased, in 1772, this forested area was a naturalist's paradise and described thus by John Evelyn, 'in the compass of twenty five miles, yet within fourteen miles of London, there is not a house, barn, church, or building, besides three lodges . . . a solitarie desert, yet stor'd with not less than three thousand deere'. Although Enfield Chase was a rather special area, Evelyn's description could have fitted smaller, but similar areas of 'desert' (complexes of woods, heaths, marshes, etc) and their stores of wildlife in contemporary Hertfordshire. Yet, apparently, these remained largely unexplored by entomologists. Almost a century was to pass before the next records become available.

North Hertfordshire Museums' Natural History Department has in its collections the closely written pages of *Joseph Ransom's Naturalist's Book*. Ransom, who lived near Hitchin and died at the early age of thirty-five, made few observations on butterflies, but he added two further species to the County List when he noted 'two Brimstone on 20th April 1813' and 'two Peacock and a Brimstone on 30th March 1814'.

James Francis Stephens, often referred to as the 'father of British entomology', was a great collector. He visited many localities in the vicinity of London, the neighbourhood of Hertford being a favourite hunting ground. In his *Illustrations of British Entomology (Haustellata)*, Volumes 1 and 4, published in 1828 and 1834, he recorded twelve further species for the county. These included Queen of Spain Fritillary 'in plenty August and September 1818', Comma 'abundant prior to 1813', Purple Emperor 'July 1833', Camberwell Beauty and Small Blue.

*An Illustrated Natural History of British Butterflies* by Edward Newman was published in 1874. This added five more species with Silver-spotted Skipper 'from Berkhamsted Common', Marbled White 'from Woodcock Hill, Elstree', Large Tortoiseshell 'from many localities', Clouded Yellow and Gatekeeper. Newman also published a record of Duke of Burgundy Fritillary 'from Berkhamsted Common', which Gibbs (1903), wrongly, considered to be erroneous.

Between 1841 and 1873 a few notes and records relating to Hertfordshire were published in contemporary journals such as *The Entomologist, The Entomologist's Annual, The Entomologist's Weekly Intelligencer* and *The Entomologist's Monthly Magazine*, but added very little to the overall picture.

In 1862 the Haileybury and Imperial Service College, near Hertford Heath, was founded. There was evidently a great passion for natural history amongst several staff and pupils for, on 6 November 1872, the Haileybury Natural Science Society was formed, with the objects of studying the wildlife of the college grounds and adjacent areas and the establishment of a museum. Under the guidance of masters, students soon began to collect all manner of specimens and make records. The Society's first *Annual Report* in 1873 listed twenty-six butterflies taken or seen around Haileybury. These included Wood White, Pearl-bordered Fritillary, Large Tortoiseshell and Purple Hairstreak. In 1875 their second *Annual Report* included local sightings of Black-veined White and Grayling. Studies continued, the museum grew as collections of all aspects of natural history, from Britain and abroad, were deposited, and in 1888 a fund of local information was published in the Society's first issue of *The Fauna and Flora of Haileybury*. This included a list of some thirty-two species of butterflies. Two further issues were published in 1902 and 1926. In the latter, forty-three species were listed, of which thirty-nine were noted as represented in the collections. Specimens still survive in the Haileybury Museum, but, most unfortunately, data labels were not attached to the majority and it is not possible to be absolutely certain of their provenances. It can be surmised that much was probably local, but, as pointed out above, material was collected from many parts of the world by students and 'old boys', and it cannot safely be used to validate published records.

An important date for the study of Hertfordshire's wildlife was 23 January 1875, when the Watford Natural History Society was founded. From the start its objects included, 'the investigation of the natural history of the neighbourhood of Watford and the County of Hertford and the dissemination of information amongst its members'. Also among its objects were 'the discouragement of the collection of rare plants and animals, the encouragement of note-taking, and the establishment of a museum'. Importantly, the officers of this Society realised the value of publishing papers and information. In 1878 the first *Transactions of the Watford Natural History Society* was published which contained a paper, read before the Society in 1875 by Arthur Cottam, entitled 'Notes on the observations of Insects in connexion with investigations of seasonal phenomena'. In this, Cottam made the first of many appeals to members to send in details of their observations, although his early requests were mainly related to the growing interest in phenological studies. Members were particularly urged to note the vernal broods of Large and Small White, the first appearances of Meadow Brown, and the occurrences of unusual numbers of Painted Lady, Clouded and Pale Clouded Yellows. Cottam made a special appeal to lady members,

> ... for so many insects are entirely day fliers, and can only be observed or taken in the mid-day sunshine, when comparatively few gentlemen have leisure or opportunity to be out in the country, that, with the butterflies especially, we shall have to trust very much our lady friends to look out for their appearance.

Unfortunately Cottam received little response, although the second, and last, *Transactions of the Watford Natural History Society* contained a paper by the Rev. C. M. Perkins (read before the Society on 14 March 1878) entitled 'On British Butterflies', which contained references to thirty-four (possibly thirty-eight) species found in the Bricket Wood and Watford region, including Silver-washed, Pearl-bordered and Small Pearl-bordered Fritillaries and Dingy and Grizzled Skippers.

Following requests to expand the scope of the Watford Society a

Special Meeting was held on 12 June 1879 and a resolution put forward to rename it as the Hertfordshire Natural History Society and Field Club. This was passed unanimously and took effect from the 1 July that year. The original objects of the Watford Society were to be continued and widened to cover the whole of the county in greater depth. The planned museum would be restricted to specimens collected in Hertfordshire only. For a long time activities of the new Society remained polarised to the south-west. However records and papers continued to be published, in a renamed journal, *The Transactions of the Hertfordshire Natural History Society*. Gradually contributions were made from other parts of the county and the *Transactions*, over a century later, continues to be an essential reference for all aspects of the county's natural history, including nearly all the published information on the county's butterflies.

First Recorder of Entomology for Hertfordshire was Miss Eleanor A. Ormerod, consulting entomologist to The Royal Agricultural Society. Her annual reports for 1881 and 1882, and those of her successor, Frank W. Silvester, for 1883 and 1884, added little to the knowledge of butterfly distribution, but included some interesting data on phenology and on effects of insect pests. The references they both made to the paucity of forthcoming notes were not completely ignored. Two papers with local listings of butterflies were submitted and accepted for publications in the *Transactions*: Arthur Griffith in 1884, noted observations and captures made by himself and his brother, F. Ll. Griffith, in the neighbourhood of Sandridge near St Albans; their collecting area, which centred upon Sandridge village, was six miles long by two miles wide and produced twenty-nine species. John Hartley Durrant's paper of 1885 recorded thirty species within a radius of about five miles of Hitchin. Durrant, an acknowledged expert on micro-moths, also published another important paper, in the *Transactions* of 1888, on 'Contributions to the entomological fauna of Hertfordshire – No.1 – Lepidoptera', from which many of the above references have been taken.

In 1879 Arthur Ernest Gibbs was elected to the Hertfordshire Natural History Society and contributed his first notes to the *Transactions* in 1881. Gibbs was very much a local man and considered by his contemporaries as one of the county's finest naturalists. Born in 1858 at St Albans, he spent most of his life there until his death in 1917. A businessman journalist by profession he was very much a naturalist at heart, and devoted much time and energy to field studies, the collection of many aspects of natural sciences, and the work of the Hertfordshire Natural History Society. From 1889 to 1899 he was Curator of the Society's collections, and it was largely through his efforts that the County Museum (now City Museum), at St Albans, was established to house the growing collections of the Society. Despite failing health Gibbs undertook the presidency of the Society from 1912 until his death. Although he studied many facets of natural history, Gibbs was particularly interested in lepidoptera and made a large collection. Unfortunately, his specimens, originally deposited in the County Museum, can no longer be traced, and it is thought that a

Figure 6.1 *A. E. Gibbs – one of Hertfordshire's pioneer naturalists produced the first County List of Lepidoptera in 1902. Photo – courtesy of City Museum, St Albans*

few possibly went to the national collections in the British Museum (Natural History). As County Recorder for lepidoptera he produced annual reports in the *Transactions* from 1892 to 1907 and corresponded with many other naturalists. His enthusiasm, knowledge and expertise drew together a core of recorders, including several from the north and east of Hertfordshire. Butterfly records accumulated to the end of the 19th century were published by Gibbs in 1902 in the *Victoria History* of the county. This noted fifty species, with some notes on status and distribution, and remained the major county list for the next thirty-five years.

No doubt prompted by Gibb's work several other entomologists published local listings in the *Transactions* between 1897 and 1916, including W. C. Boyd (1901), with twenty-five species from the Cheshunt area, and Dr A. H. Foster (1916) with forty-three species found in north Hertfordshire. Gibbs's paper in the *Transactions* of 1916, on 'The Satyrid butterflies of Hertfordshire, with a short study of *Pararge aegeria*', apparently ended an era for, apart from notes on Black-veined White and Bath White seen in the county and published in 1921, there were few further references to butterflies in the *Transactions* until 1936. However, several entomologists were active until the Second World War, their collections and field notebooks providing most useful evidence for the later determinations of changes in status of many species. Some of these collections survive and are noted in Table 6.1 which lists all the known major collections of butterflies still to be found in Hertfordshire, with dates of collection and the holding institutions. There may be other important collections in private hands, although no information has been forwarded.

Of particular interest are the detailed diaries on the butterflies of west Hertfordshire kept by the late S. B. Hodgson of Berkhamsted. He noted forty species between 1931 and 1961, detailing early and late occurrences and habitat changes affecting many species. Some of his notes were published in the *Transactions* of 1936, 1938, 1939 and 1962.

Following the death of A. E. Gibbs, Dr Arthur Herbert Foster was appointed County Recorder for lepidoptera, a post he held until his own death. Foster was Medical Officer at the Hitchin Union Work

House from 1908. An avid collector, of both butterflies and moths, he appears to have remained rather remote from many of his contemporaries. For twenty years he gathered together information for his major works. These were the sections on vertebrates, butterflies and moths in *The Natural History of the Hitchin Region*, edited by R. L. Hine, and published in 1934, and 'A List of the Lepidoptera of Hertfordshire' in the *Transactions* of 1937, with addenda and corrigenda in 1940, 1941, 1942, 1944 and 1946. The 'List' brought together all the then known data on butterflies and moths. It contains fifty-four butterfly species, with some indications of status and has remained the standard reference for the county for over half a century. Foster died in 1946, leaving extensive and important collections which are now housed in the Natural History Department of North Hertfordshire Museums. During his long tenure of office as County Recorder, however, he produced only one annual report – for 1945; this was published in the *Transactions* of 1946, and only listed eight correspondents who submitted records. The rigours of the Second World War and its aftermath radically changed natural history. Many good field recorders passed away, attitudes and fashions towards wildlife studies

TABLE 6.1   *Major collections of butterflies still to be found in Hertfordshire*

| Collection | Approximate dates of collection | Holding institution |
|---|---|---|
| Haileybury Natural Science Society | 1873 to c 1950 | Haileybury College |
| ‡Letchworth Naturalists' Society | 1880 to 1970 | North Herts Museums |
| ‡Dr W. P. Grellet | 1889 to 1912 | North Herts Museums |
| *L. W. Newman | 1891 to 1934 | City Museum, St Albans |
| C. Mellows | 1900 to 1956 | Bishops Stortford College |
| ‡S. Pearce | 1900 to 1925 | North Herts Museum |
| L. S. Hodson | 1902 to 1956 | City Museum, St Albans |
| *G. H. E. Hopkins | 1907 to 1969 | City Museum, St Albans |
| A. Bell | 1910 to 1930 | Welwyn/Hatfield Museum |
| ‡Dr A. H. Foster | 1910 to 1935 | North Herts Museums |
| *H. A. Leeds | 1918 to 1929 | City Museum, St Albans |
| *A. E. Stafford | 1921 to 1923 | City Museum, St Albans |
| *G. E. Tite | 1926 to 1955 | City Museum, St Albans |
| *A. L. Goodson | 1930 to 1951 | City Museum, St Albans |
| G. Graverley Edwards | 1932 to 1972 | City Museum, St Albans |
| *O. A. Alexander | ?      to 1955 | City Museum, St Albans |
| R. S. Ferry | 1938 to 1977 | Welwyn/Hatfield Museum |
| ‡S. Woodall | 1967 to 1977 | North Herts Museums |

*These collections are now combined into one at the City Museum, St Albans and known as the Hopkins/Alexander Collection.   ‡North Herts Museums' Natural History Department, Baldock.

Figure 6.2 *Knebworth Woods, like so many other areas has unfortunately lost many interesting butterflies*

changed and the malignant deterioration of our countryside accelerated.

From 1946 to 1981 an unbroken series of annual lepidoptera reports by County Recorders were published in the *Transactions*. Those for 1946 and 1947 were contributed by Sir John Fryer, former Director of the Ministry of Agriculture Plant Pathology Laboratory at Harpenden, whose second report, published posthumously, introduced a format relating records to weather. He was followed by Peter J. Bell, who held the office of County Recorder from 1950 until his retirement in 1976. Bell, an agricultural journalist, had the invidious task of documenting the worst period, to date, that our butterflies have had to face, with dramatic variations in weather patterns, revolutionary changes in agriculture, dereliction of woods and coppices, loss of grasslands, urban expansion and rising atmospheric pollution. There was also a dearth of competent field naturalists, records were rather scant and several species of butterflies declined or disappeared from certain areas virtually unnoticed, despite Bell's continued pleas for records.

Peter Waterton, elected County Recorder in 1976, also made appeals for more records in his annual reports covering the years 1977 to 1981. Since 1939, only four papers giving local lists of butterflies had been published in the *Transactions*. L. S. Hodson (1939) related the Hatfield district for 1937 and 1938, S. B. Hodgson referred to west Hertfordshire in 1939 and 1962, and R. J. Penrose (1980) listed observations in the Watford area from 1939 to 1962. Following my decision to organise the Hertfordshire Butterfly Atlas Project, Peter Waterton prepared a paper on 'The distribution of butterflies in Hertfordshire – 1970 to 1981', which was published in the *Transactions* of 1984. This listed forty-nine species with thirty-nine provisional distribution maps and some outlines regarding status. There were many obvious gaps, and it was concern over the decline of many species, plus an apparent lack of conservation and real knowledge of the current status of both rarities and some of the 'more common' butterflies, which provided a spur for the Atlas Project fieldwork and this book.

# 7

# The Hertfordshire Butterfly Atlas Project (*The Survey*)

The Hertfordshire Butterfly Atlas Project was established in 1983 with the assistance of the Hertfordshire Natural History Society. It was widely advertised through journals, local press and radio and, individually, to members of the Society and other entomological groups. People interested in participating were issued with a set of instructions, recording cards and sent annual newsletters outlining progress. To ensure full coverage of all parts of the county, particularly in the final year of fieldwork, a number of recorders undertook specific survey areas.

During the field seasons of the 1984 to 1986 Survey, Hertfordshire's butterflies received more concentrated attention than at any earlier time. Nearly 200 fieldworkers submitted some 20 000 records in a variety of formats from casual sightings to most detailed lists of specific areas. Incoming data were checked and collated by hand at North Hertfordshire Museums' Natural History Department, and mapped, compatibly with other county recording schemes, on the *tetrad* basis. (A tetrad is a two-kilometre square – four of the small squares bounded by even-numbered kilometre lines of the National Grid, on Ordnance

Figure 7.1 *Map showing the number of butterfly species recorded per tetrad from 1970 to 1986*

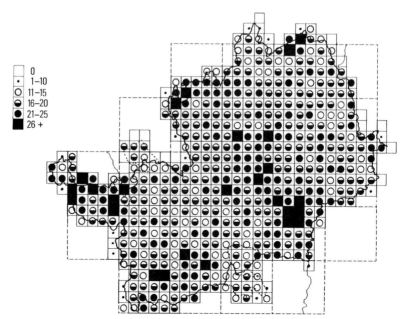

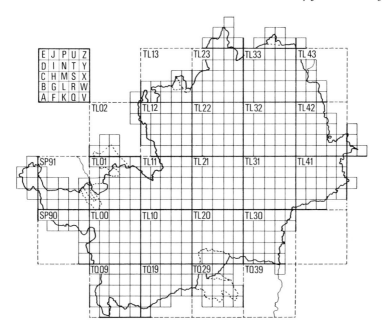

Figure 7.2 *Map showing the tetrad notation for Hertfordshire*

Survey maps – *see* Appendix 2.) All major sites noted in the text are listed in Appendix 3 with their appropriate tetrad references.

All available past and present collections, notebooks, manuscripts and literature references were examined for further data. These data were entered on to record cards and also mapped, with a distinction between pre- and post-1970 records. Only two date-classes were chosen, partly because of the impreciseness of some of the early data – many of the older entomologists were prone to omitting localities for species they regarded as common, but mainly to link with other local and national recording schemes. Conveniently, many environmental changes affecting butterfly populations can also be related to these periods. Experience of other publications shows that too many symbols tend to make maps illegible.

All Butterfly Atlas field records and other data have been deposited in the collections of the North Hertfordshire Museums' Natural History Department at Baldock, where it may be consulted by appointment.

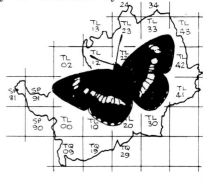

# 8

# Hertfordshire's Butterflies – Past and Present

Including residents, migrants, vagrants, accidentals and extinct species, there are 105 butterflies on the full British List (Bradley and Fletcher 1979). About sixty species are still, more or less, regularly recorded in the British Isles and fifty-four are now accepted on to the all-time list for Hertfordshire. Table 8.1 shows how these are categorised. Records of nine further species have been published for the county; all are rather inadequately substantiated with specimens and data, and so, although they are mentioned in the species accounts, they have not been accepted on to the County List. These species (indicated by square brackets) are Chequered Skipper, Oberthur's Grizzled Skipper, Swallowtail, Black Hairstreak, Large Copper, Silver-studded Blue, Mazarine Blue, Large Blue and American Painted Lady.

Information available from some of the counties adjacent to Hertfordshire shows that Bedfordshire and Buckinghamshire both have total lists of fifty-four species also, including twelve and three extinct species respectively, and Essex has forty-eight species of which nine are extinct.

With the exception of a few rare vagrants, all species on the Hertfordshire List have been mapped, including some which are now extinct. Since 1970, forty-six species have been recorded for the county, with forty during the 1984 to 1986 Survey. The species not encountered during the Survey were Wood White, Camberwell Beauty,

TABLE 8.1  *Categorisation of the fifty-four butterfly species on the all-time list for Hertfordshire (to 1986)*

| Category | Number of species | Details |
|---|---|---|
| Extinct species (former residents) | 7 | Silver-spotted Skipper, Adonis Blue, Small Pearl-bordered Fritillary; Pearl-bordered Fritillary, High Brown Fritillary, Marsh Fritillary, Grayling |
| Regular migrants | 3 | Red Admiral, Painted Lady, Clouded Yellow (which may also breed) |
| Vagrants | 9 | Large Tortoiseshell and Wood White are former residents. |
| Residents | 35 | |

30

Queen of Spain Fritillary, Grayling, High Brown and Pearl-bordered Fritillaries.

Mainly as a result of the Survey, records have been made in all of the 576 whole or part tetrads of Hertfordshire. (*See* Figure 7.1). Except for a few tetrads, containing only small portions of the county, all the rest have had eleven or more species recorded. Since 1970, twenty-one or more species have been recorded in 149 tetrads, the 'top three' having thirty-four, thirty-two and thirty species respectively. (*See* Table 10.2.) The eleven most frequently recorded butterflies in the county were, in descending order of abundance of records received, Meadow Brown, Small Tortoiseshell, Small White, Peacock, Gatekeeper, Large White, Green-veined White, Orange Tip, Comma, Small Skipper and Brimstone.

Most of the species distribution maps are considered to be fairly comprehensively complete, although a few species, for example Essex Skipper and Purple Hairsteak, are almost certainly under-recorded. There are some parts of the county, notably in east Hertfordshire and the region to the north of Hemel Hempstead, that receive rather too little attention from naturalists and might repay further fieldwork.

# 9

# Species Accounts

The taxonomic order and nomenclature used throughout the species accounts follows that of Bradley and Fletcher (1979). All present scientific systems for naming animals and plants are based upon Linnaeus's binomial system, using Latin. Each organism is allocated two names, the generic name, which has a capital initial, followed by a specific or trivial name, now always with a small initial, for example Pearl-bordered Fritillary is *Boloria euphrosyne*. After first mention, generic names may be abbreviated to their initial, so that Small Pearl-bordered Fritillary may be *B. selene*. Strictly the trivial name should be followed, in full or abbreviated, by that of the author who first gave the organism its present trivial name; in the case of the Pearl-bordered Fritillary this was Linnaeus, who is commonly abbreviated to L., making *Boloria euphrosyne* L. If an animal was later reclassified by another author into a different genus, the original namer is placed in brackets thus (L.) Botanical nomenclature differs in that the reclassifier's name is also given, e.g. the Field Scabious is called *Knautia arvensis* (L.) Coulter, because Linnaeus first named it *Scabiosa arvensis*, but later Coulter removed it to the genus *Knautia*. Subspecies are indicated through the use of the second trivial name.

The species accounts give an assessment of past and present distribution and status of Hertfordshire's butterflies, with references to national trends. Some guidelines for the identification and ecology of each species are given. Heading each account is the date of the first recorded occurrence, and the recorder or earliest known published reference for the county. With many species, first emergences and subsequent duration of flight periods may vary from year to year; the earliest and latest observation dates within Hertfordshire are shown, indicating the considerable differences that may be encountered. Perhaps also, some competitive further research and recording may be engendered to expand these data.

The photographs, many of which were taken in Hertfordshire, are intended primarily to provide an introduction to the range and beauty of our butterflies and their habitats. Many good identification guides are available which will supplement the brief details given here. Particularly recommended are Thomas (1986), Higgins and Riley (1980) and Carter (1981).

Three symbols are used on the species distribution maps in the species accounts; these indicate

○   pre-1970 records

●   post-1970 records (most of which relate to the 1984–1986 Survey)

X   known post-1970 introductions

A map outlining some of the major areas for butterflies in Hertford-shire can be found on the endpapers of this book.

The *Transactions of the Hertfordshire Natural History Society* will, hopefully, remain for a long time to come, a resource for publication of future research to expand the details and scope of this book and, through the County Recorder for Lepidoptera, to publish an ongoing series of records for the butterflies of Hertfordshire.

# [Chequered Skipper

*Carterocephalus palaemon* Pallas ]

Foster (1941) makes the only reference to Chequered Skipper in Hert-fordshire, through a note, sent to him by a Mr Gerard, claiming the species from Ware, with 'one taken in 1933 flying over rough grass near a pine wood, and probably another seen'. The authenticity of this specimen, which does not appear to have survived, was never authoritatively checked and the record cannot be admitted to the County List. Perhaps, as sometimes happened elsewhere, Gerard's specimens were well-marked female Large Skippers. Chequered Skip-pers are, however, quite distinctive, the upperwings having prominent bright yellow spots on a dark brown-to-black ground. Underwings bear the same patterning on a greenish-grey ground. Hertfordshire, as detailed in Heath, Pollard and Thomas (1984), has always been outside the acceptable documented range of this species. It was first discovered for Britain at Clapham Park Wood, Bedfordshire in 1798, and was always locally restricted to ancient semi-natural woods of mainly the Midlands, northern Lincolnshire and a part of western Scotland. Sadly the English populations declined dramatically in the 1960s and it was declared extinct in 1980. Fortunately the Scottish populations remain in a healthy state.

# Small Skipper

*Thymelicus sylvestris* Poda

J. F. Stephens – 1828

With the exception of much of northern England, the mountainous parts of Wales, the whole of Scotland and Ireland, Small Skipper is common. Its well defined southerly distribution is regulated by climatic limitations. In Hertfordshire most areas of tall grassland support colonies which may be much larger than casual observations

PLATE
page 38

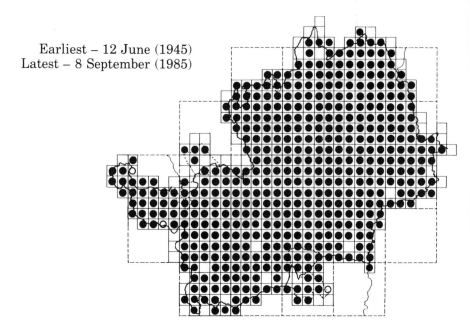

Earliest – 12 June (1945)
Latest – 8 September (1985)

would suggest. At times, many more adults will be at rest amongst
the grasses than are flying or feeding. There may also be a good
proportion of their congener, the very similar Essex Skipper (*see
below*) in such colonies. Short, grazed or cut, swards are unsuitable.
Records show that Small Skipper remains quite common and widespread throughout the county although local declines have resulted
from urbanisation and the intensification of agriculture. Almost any
road verge, railway embankment, wood margin and patch of rough
grassland, including the less intensively managed garden lawns, will
hold at least some Small Skippers. They are less frequent on the
Boulder Clay soils of north-east Hertfordshire but can occur in very
large numbers elsewhere, particularly in years when grazing or
cutting is abandoned.

Named from their delightful darting, 'skipping flight' Small Skippers have bright orange-brown upperwings with black margins and
white fringes to the trailing edges. Males have a long, fairly thick,
oblique black scent mark across the upper forewings. The unpatterned
underwings are duller and tinged with grey-green. In common with
some of the other skippers, they usually bask with the hindwings held
flat and the forewings raised obliquely above them. To be absolutely
certain of avoiding confusion with Essex Skippers it is necessary to
examine closely the undersides of the tips of the antennae; these are
orange to brown on Small Skippers as opposed to jet-black on Essex
Skippers.

Several 'soft' grasses are mentioned as food plants of larvae in
many texts, but recent research has shown that mature Yorkshire Fog
*Holcus lanatus* L. is most preferred. This is a species which is rapidly
removed by intensive cultivation or improvement of grasslands. Egg-
laying females search the dying flower heads of grasses and lay eggs,
sometimes up to ten per plant, in the sheaths throughout July. Larvae
emerge in August and immediately construct silken hibernation
chambers. In the following spring they disperse and commence feeding

on fresh blades of grass. This behaviour pattern protects the larvae from the risk of late summer drought and desiccation of foodplants and was almost certainly a major factor in preventing the decline of the Small Skipper following the severe drought of 1976, which significantly reduced the populations of several other grassland species with active late summer larvae. Small Skipper larvae bind grass blades together with silken threads to form tubes within which they feed. Later, as they grow, they venture out to produce characteristic wedge-shaped notches in the leaves.

Following pupation within a loose cocoon of silk spun amongst the grass leaves, the main flight period is from late June to mid-August, a few worn specimens often persisting into September. The aptly named 'skippers' are an attractive, yet difficult group of butterflies to observe and further information is required, particularly on the local ecological relationships between Small and Essex Skippers.

# Essex Skipper

*Thymelicus lineola*   Ochsenheimer

A. J. Spiller – 1885

Essex Skipper is almost certainly under-recorded in Hertfordshire so that the distribution map is somewhat incomplete. This reflects the difficulties of differentiating Essex from Small Skippers. The two species are frequently found together, especially when feeding on patches of knapweeds, thistles or brambles. Distinction is impossible when they are on the wing and even when they are settled a good close view is necessary. As noted with the previous species, the most

PLATE
page 38

Earliest – 13 June (1929)
Latest – 30 August (1985)

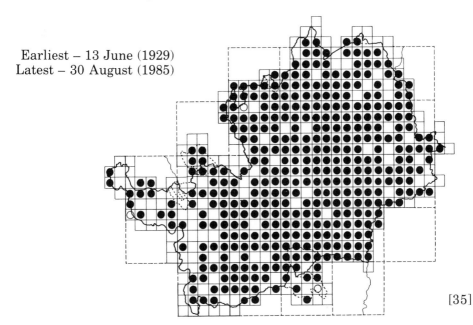

[35]

reliable characteristic is colouration of the undersides of the antennal tips. These are generally jet-black in the Essex Skipper and orange to brown in the Small Skipper. However, care should be exercised, for Small Skippers may be encountered with dark uppersides to their antennae and brown under-tips, and some Essex Skippers, notably late females, can have a pronounced brownish tinge to the lower antennal tips. Male Essex Skippers have less distinct, finer, scent marks running parallel to the leading edges of the forewings.

Interestingly the Essex Skipper was noted by A. J. Spiller (in the *Transactions of the Bishops Stortford Natural History Society* (1950) as 'plentiful in our town district from 1885 to 1888'. This pre-dates the addition of Essex Skipper to the British List in 1889, when F. W. Hawes realised the distinctions between the Small and Essex Skippers from specimens collected in Essex. If only Hertfordshire lepidopterists had published their observations more promptly this species might easily have been called the 'Stortford' or the 'Hertfordshire Skipper'.

Gibbs (1902) did not note Essex Skipper, but in 1905 and 1906 a few, confined to small areas, were reported from Chalk downs near Aldbury in the south-west of Hertfordshire. In August 1910 a specimen, thought by Gibbs (1911) to be the first for the county, was taken at Therfield Heath by the Rev. G. H. Raynor, and presented to Gibbs for his collections at the County Museum. It was probable that the species had been in Hertfordshire, in small numbers, for some time and there are contemporary records for Bedfordshire. Certainly a range-expansion was occurring, for by the 1920s several entomologists were reporting the Essex Skipper as 'common' in parts of north Hertfordshire, and by the mid-1940s it was abundant on the Chalk and Boulder Clay near Royston and Barkway. In 1945 the Rev. W. Greenham wrote to Foster '*lineola* common in Walkern area, more so than *sylvestris*. In the lane from Walkern Church one first encounters *sylvestris* for about sixty yards and then as one approaches the chalk pit one finds *lineola*, but hardly any *sylvestris*. The two species are not mixed up to any extent'. Perhaps this is a slight key to the ecological differences of the two species, although in the county good colonies of Essex Skipper are not confined to calcareous grasslands. Reasonable, and sometimes large, numbers may be found in many types of grass-land including those that are more acid or rank. Its true distribution in the county appears to match closely that of the Small Skipper and colonies have been noticeably increasing along trunk road verges. The apparent scarcity in the west of the county may well be due to under-recording, although further detailed studies would be worthwhile.

Essex Skippers' eggs are laid on the tight sheaths of grasses, mainly Cocks-foot *Dactylis glomerata* L. and Creeping Soft Grass *Holcus mollis* L., but False Brome *Brachypodium sylvaticum* (Hudson) Beauv., Tor Grass *B. pinnatum* (L.) Beauv. and Timothy *Phleum pratense* L. have also occasionally been noted. Hatching occurs in the following spring and the larvae are active by day, leaving tubes spun from leaf blades to feed. Pupation takes place within a cocoon formed amongst grass leaves. Generally adult Essex Skippers emerge about a fortnight later than Small Skippers, but there may be considerable overlap of the species as the main flight period of the former lasts from late June to early August.

# Silver-spotted Skipper

## *Hesperia comma* Linnaeus

The Rev. G. H. Raynor – 1874

Formerly locally common in discrete areas of very short-grazed open   PLATE
turf on the Chalk escarpment, the Silver-spotted Skipper is now   page 39
extinct in Hertfordshire. It is now one of Britain's rarest resident
butterflies, and the local demise, which was fairly well documented,
closely parallels the severe national decline of the past thirty years.
Newman (1874) published the earliest county reference with a record
made by the Rev. G. H. Raynor at Berkhamsted Common. Another

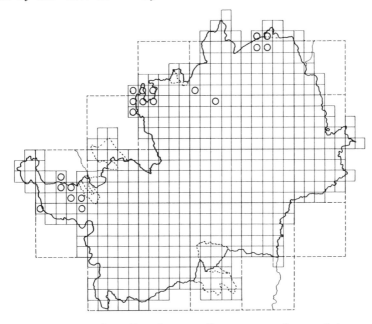

record in Newman, from Broxbourne Common, and some later reports
from Haileybury, Watery Grove near Knebworth and Hitch Wood are
unacceptable, as these locations have never supported the right type
of habitat, and certainly no specimens were put forward to substan-
tiate the claims of the observers. From 1897 to 1899 Cottam (1900)
found Silver-spotted Skippers to be 'local' on the Chalk downs at
Aldbury. Later records suggested that populations were prone to fluctuations related to the weather of late summer. In 1902 and 1906 the
species was 'plentiful at Aldbury Downs', but 'not so common' at
Aldbury Nowers in 1908. Foster (1916) found Silver-spotted Skippers
to be 'common, often abundant on Therfield Heath', and 'in limited
spots, sometimes quite commonly on the Pegsdon Hills (partially in
Bedfordshire to the west of Hitchin)'. A specimen was obtained at
Letchworth Hall in 1916 and reported in the Annual Lepidoptera
Report to the Letchworth Naturalists' Society. Records show that
despite periodic fluctuations good populations remained in the main

Plate 1    (*Top*)  Small Skipper (*Thymelicus sylvestris* [p. 33]
          (*Bottom*)  Essex Skipper (*Thymelicus lineola*) (note that undersides of
          antennal tips are jet black) [p. 35]

Plate 2 (*Top*) Silver-spotted Skipper (*Hesperia comma*) [p. 37]
(*Bottom*) Large Skipper (*Ochlodes venata*) [p. 41]

sites near Aldbury, on the hills about Pegsdon and Hexton and at Therfield Heath, until the early 1950s.

About 1940 the Rev. W. Greenham of Walkern informed Foster that Silver-spotted Skippers were to be found near Gravely (probably Ledgeside Plantation, formerly Chalk grassland now thick scrub and trees), although Foster could find no trace there in 1944 or 1945. After a visit to Therfield Heath, on 10 August 1945, to collect specimens, Greenham again wrote to Foster ' – gave me as many as I wanted – and easy to catch on the dwarf thistle'. Roger Ferry collected eighteen specimens there on 27 August 1946.

In his diaries S. B. Hodgson wrote that prior to 1949 the Silver-spotted Skipper was 'fairly common' at Aldbury Nowers, but 'in 1947 it was collected for Tring Museum [from both Aldbury Nowers and the adjacent Pitstone Hill in Buckinghamshire] too heavily in my opinion and has been scarcer each year'. In the Hopkins/Alexander collections at St Albans Museum are thirteen specimens taken from the same sites between 1949 and 1955, including seven obtained in 1955. Quite suddenly the Silver-spotted Skipper disappeared from all sites, the last county records being from the Hexton area about 1950, Aldbury Nowers on 23 August 1957 and Therfield Heath in 1959. Over-collection may have hastened local extinction, but the major factors were the losses of suitable habitats and a series of poor summers, as occurred during the 1950s and 1960s.

Silver-spotted Skippers thrive in a dry micro-climate and occur in Britain at the northern edge of their European range. They can still be found at a few sites in southern England, but are only active on the warmer sunny days of their flight period which lasts throughout August and into early September. The larger females have dark brown upperwings with conspicuous yellow-gold markings. Males are duller, with a black scent line across the upper forewings. Underwings of both sexes are olive-green with distinctive silver patches, which gave the species its vernacular name. On cursory examination some late flying and faded Large Skippers may be easily mistaken for the Silver-spotted.

The overwintering eggs are laid singly on low growing tufts of Sheep's Fescue *Festuca ovina* L., growing in open, south-facing situations, usually on relatively bare or disturbed ground such as track-sides or Rabbit scrapes. Larvae feed on the fine leaves from a 'tent' and pupation takes place at the base of the plants. Formerly much of the downland would have had very short-cropped open swards with many bare patches maintained by Sheep and Rabbits. Cessation of Sheep grazing and the almost complete elimination of the Rabbit population following the introduction of the myxomatosis virus in 1954 facilitated rapid habitat changes. Overgrowth of coarser grasses and scrub soon followed, completely changing the character of the downs. Even before myxomatosis extensive areas of former downs were ploughed or subjected to agricultural improvement at the expense of their butterfly populations.

Rabbits are once again increasing and it is possible that Sheep farming may return on a large scale if subsidies improve profitability for farmers. Suitable sites may then become available for carefully controlled re-introductions of the Silver-spotted Skipper.

# Large Skipper

*Ochlodes venata*  Bremer and Grey

J. F. Stephens – 1828

Intensification of agriculture, shading of woods, removal of hedges and the loss of grasslands have reduced populations of the Large Skipper in Hertfordshire. However it remains relatively common and widespread, and sometimes large colonies may be found on unimproved grassland. The distribution map does not clearly show the relative scarcity in the arable and urban parts of the county, for it may still be found in these areas, but in small numbers, on grassy road verges, railway embankments and waste land.

PLATE
page 39

Earliest – 21 May (1945)
Latest – 22 August (1986)

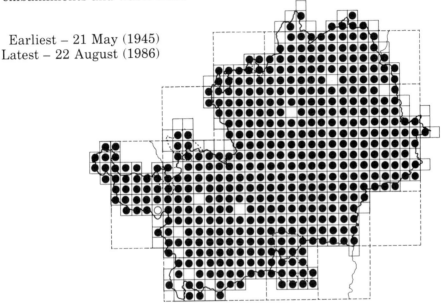

Like most of the other skippers Large Skippers fly only in sunshine but they have a greater preference for sheltered localities than either Small or Essex Skippers. They can be distinguished from these by their slightly larger size and distinctive brown, orange-mottled and black-veined wings; the general wing colouration is more pronounced in females, but males have a large scent mark across the middle of each upper forewing, underwings are duller green-brown with faint markings. The main flight time is June and July, and between bursts of 'skipping' flights and feeding on brambles, knapweeds and thistles, Large Skippers spend long periods at rest. Colonies may often be much larger than at first appreciated for, at any one time, many individuals will be at rest amongst the grasses. Males also often hold prominent perches, from which they make rapid darting flights in pursuit of passing females.

Eggs are laid singly beneath the leaf blades of the preferred food

41

plant of the larvae, Cocks-foot *Dactylis glomerata* L., although False Brome *Brachypodium sylvaticum* (Hudson) Beauv. has occasionally been known to support small colonies. The newly emerged larvae form feeding tubes from rolled leaf blades held by silken threads. When about half-grown they enter hibernation within a similar construction formed from several leaf blades. Feeding resumes in the following spring and the full-grown larvae are bluish-green with a darker green line down their backs. Pupation takes place within a cocoon formed from grass blades drawn together by silk.

# Dingy Skipper

*Erynnis tages*   Linnaeus

J. F. Stephens – 1828

PLATE
page 58

Dingy Skipper has gone from several of its former haunts, particularly across central Hertfordshire. Foster (1916) noted this species – aptly named from its drab and inconspicuous colouration, but none-the-less attractive – as widely distributed and common in north Hertfordshire, sometimes locally abundant on downs, railway banks and commons and, in his 'List' (1937), as 'recorded from all districts: often common'. Some substantial colonies were noted from near Bishops Stortford, Hertford Heath and Whippendell Woods near Watford in the early 1950s, after which a general decline was noted. Despite Foster's sweeping statements, the Dingy Skipper was probably never really as widespread as they would suggest, although many colonies have been lost to agriculture, and others as woodland rides, wood pastures,

Earliest – 30 April (1957)
Latest – 17 June (1906)

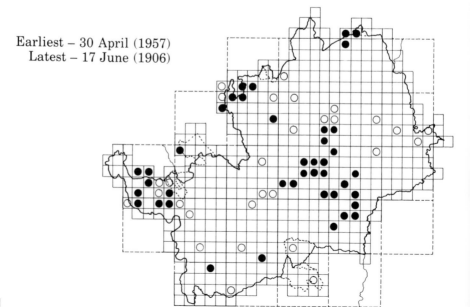

[42]

commons and grasslands have become shaded or improved. Regular sightings are still made of small numbers from the more favoured localities on the drier soils of the Chalk and gravels. Typical of these are the grasslands about Tring and Ashridge, Hexton and Pegsdon and Therfield Heath, and the wide grassy rides of woods in the Broxbourne, Welwyn Garden City, Tewin and Bramfield areas. Some isolated colonies are known and it is probable that with further detailed searching more will be found.

Major factors associated wihh the decline of Dingy Skipper were again the disappearance of Rabbits and poor summers in the 1950s. Without Rabbits, larval foodplants were suppressed by the encroachment of more vigorous plants, and bare patches of soil, essential for 'sunning' Dingy Skippers, were lost. Common Blues, which utilise the same foodplants (except Horseshoe Vetch), probably remain more widespread because they 'sun' more frequently on flowers or amongst grasses. Dingy Skipper is also a less mobile species and lacks potential to spread.

Usually in quite discrete colonies, Dingy Skippers are on the wing from mid-May to mid-June. A partial second brood has been noted in parts of southern Britain but never in Hertfordshire. Between erratic, rather 'moth-like' flights they may spend long periods basking on patches of open ground, stones or even animal droppings. Here, the attractive subtle grey-brown patterned upperwings with light grey fringes can be most appreciated. Underwings are pale grey-brown. Males can be distinguished by a fold along the basal half of the front margin of their darker wings. In cool weather and at night these butterflies appear even more 'moth-like' as they rest with their wings draped around dead flower heads, often knapweeds. They may be mistaken for the day-flying moths, Common Heath *Ematurga atomaria* L. or Mother Shipton *Callistege mi* Clerck., both of which are on the wing at the same time as Dingy Skipper.

Most colonies of Dingy Skipper breed on Bird's-foot Trefoil *Lotus corniculatus* L., but on heavier soils Large Bird's-foot Trefoil *L. uliginosus* Schkuhr. may be used, and on the Chalk sometimes Horseshoe Vetch *Hippocrepis comosa* L. Single eggs are laid low down on tender leaves of the foodplants. Larvae feed from within a tent spun from a few leaflets. Full grown in August, they form a more substantial hibernaculum, within which they overwinter and then pupate in the following spring.

# Grizzled Skipper

*Pyrgus malvae*   Linnaeus

J. F. Stephens – 1828

Gibbs (1902) and Foster (1916 and 1937) regarded the Grizzled Skipper as locally common in Hertfordshire. Its past and present distributions and reasons for decline closely parallel those of the Dingy Skipper.

PLATE
page 58

43

Earliest – 9 April (1893)
Latest – 30 June (1954)

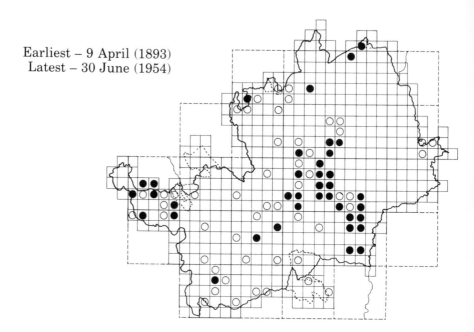

Both species may have been, and perhaps remain, under-recorded because of their colouration, the Dingy blending well with surrounding vegetation and soil, and the Grizzled's blurring flight making it almost invisible and easily 'lost' against the background of flowers and grasses. Also, in good years, that is, when there is a warm sunny spring, Grizzled Skippers may be on the wing in mid-April and over before the end of May, thereby avoiding the attentions of 'fairweather naturalists'. The usual flight period is from early-May to mid-June. A partial second brood has only rarely been noted from Hertfordshire.

As with the Dingy Skipper, the decline of the Grizzled Skipper began in the 1950s and 1960s. Late cold springs were certainly a limiting factor, and one that was accentuated by loss and deterioration of habitat. Local extinctions and reductions in populations followed as grasslands were ploughed or improved and woodland rides and clearings became shaded. As with so many other species the demise of Rabbits was of paramount importance. Small numbers are still to be found in discrete areas at Aldbury Nowers, Ashridge, Therfield Heath, in the Mimram valley, Bramfield and Broxbourne Woods. A few further isolated colonies occur, mainly in the south of the county, and it is quite possible that some new sites await discovery. Rough unimproved pastures within or adjacent to woodlands, including rides even in conifer plantations, scrubby heaths and small patches of short Chalk grassland are worth searching. Grizzled Skippers were only recently found on a small area of Chalk grassland at Baldock which had been quite closely watched by naturalists for several years.

There are two day-flying moths which do have a superficial resemblance to Grizzled Skippers, Common Heath *Ematurga atomaria* L. and Latticed Heath *Semiothisa clathrata* (L.), but when this small butterfly is settled its delicate but distinctive black and white chequerboard upperwings make it quite unmistakable. Males are rather lighter in colour and females have a marked fold on the leading edge of the forewings.

After their overwintering in the pupal stage, Grizzled Skippers' emergence and mating flights are dictated by the vagaries of spring weather. Breeding sites are sunny sheltered locations such as woodland rides and clearings, margins of scrub and grassy banks, usually with rather sparse, but not necessarily short, vegetation. Several members of the Rose family may be selected for egg laying, including Wild Strawberry *Fragaria vesca* L., Barren Strawberry *Potentilla sterilis* (L.) Garcke, Tormentil *P. erecta* (L.) Raüschel, Silverweed *P. anserina* L. and Creeping Cinquefoil *P. reptans* L. Agrimony *Agrimonia eupatoria* L., Raspberry *Rubus idaeus* L. and brambles *R. fruticosus* agg. have also been noted. Eggs are deposited singly, usually beneath small leaves. Newly emerged larvae form silken shelters from which they feed, and later entire leaves are spun together. Pupation occurs on or near to the ground in a silken cocoon.

# [Oberthür's Grizzled Skipper]

## *Pyrgus armoricanus* Oberthür

Foster (1937) lists a record, communicated to him by H. M. Edelsten, of a specimen of Oberthür's Grizzled Skipper 'taken near Haileybury on 20th May 1897, and was identified by the Nat. Hist. Museum'. This butterfly is an extremely rare vagrant to the British Isles. Only three specimens exist in the national collections of the British Museum (Natural History), with two from Norfolk without further data, and one from the Edelsten Collection. Although the Edelsten specimen is genuine it lacks data labels. It is the opinion of David Carter, of the Natural History Museum (personal communication), that 1897 is probably too early for Edelsten to have collected this specimen himself. Surprisingly, full details of this 'capture' were not published, and there is therefore some doubt clouding the authenticity of this species for Hertfordshire. Unless further details are found the record will remain unacceptable to the County List.

Oberthür's Grizzled Skipper is widely distributed in flowery meadows across central and southern Europe, becoming more local as far north as Denmark, Germany and Poland. In the south it has two broods on the wing in May/June and August/September, and a single in the north during June/July. Identification of this species is rather difficult, for there are many closely related species.

# Swallowtail

*Papilio machaon* Linnaeus

Pollard and Thomas (1984) point out the problems of separating old records of the British and continental sub-species of *Papilio machaon*. There is evidence to show that the British sub-species, *britannicus*, now confined to the Norfolk Broads, was in the past more widespread in fens of eastern England, and that the continental sub-species, *bigeneratus*, which is known to migrate, was resident in the south in the early 19th century. Swallowtail has for a long time also been a favourite species for captive breeding and attempted introductions. Without specimens to back them up, all Hertfordshire records have been treated circumspectly and the species is retained in square brackets.

The earliest report of Swallowtail in the county was made in the notebook of Edward Manser, one of the well known Quaker family of Hertford, who had a deep interest in and love of natural history. He simply stated 'fens near Hertford in 1839'. Although extensive wetlands existed in that area, the only known foodplant of the British sub-species of Swallowtail, Milk Parsley *Peucedanum palustre* (L.) Moench, has never been recorded from Hertfordshire (Dony, 1967). There are very old, and rather vague, pre-Linnaean references, made by John Ray (late 17th century), to the occurrence of Milk Parsley on the edge of Epping Forest near Roydon, Essex, not far from the border with Hertfordshire. It is possible that Manser saw a continental migrant, but it is most unlikely that there was a breeding population, for Wild Carrot *Daucus carota* L., the main larval foodplant of the few temporary colonies of continental Swallowtail known from Britain, is a plant of dry calcareous soils. Sometime before 1940 a Swallowtail was alleged to have been seen at Bishops Stortford, and there was another alleged sighting at Therfield Heath on 3 July 1945; both of these events may be connected with an immigration, particularly the latter, for many Swallowtails were noted in England in that year. The latest sighting was of one in a garden at Letchworth on 4 August 1975, which was almost certainly an escape from captivity.

Perhaps on the basis of the 1945 record Swallowtail could be admitted to the County List, but in the absence of firm data or a specimen I have erred on the side of caution and omitted it.

# Wood White

## *Leptidea sinapsis* Linnaeus

A. E. Pollock – 1871

Only a single breeding colony of the Wood White has ever been known for Hertfordshire. This was first documented, from Balls Wood near Hertford Heath, by A. E. Pollock, a member of the Haileybury Natural Science Society, in 1871. Always small, the colony remained there until the late 1970s when it was decimated by a single collector. An event which shows just how vulnerable some of our butterflies are. The last confirmed reports from Balls Wood were of single sightings

PLATE
page 59

Earliest – 5 June (1976)
Latest – 9 August (1938)

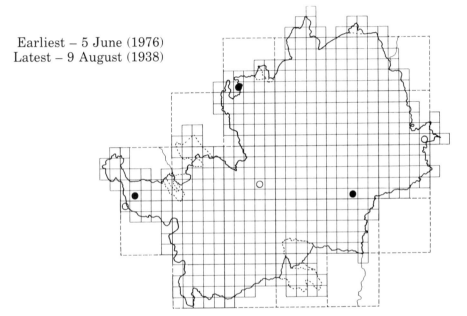

in 1976. It would appear that the colony has gone, although a possible sighting in July 1984 does raise some slight hopes of survival and further searching would be worthwhile in this area.

There have been a few other records of single sightings. The only one from the east of the county was made in the grounds of the Nonconformist Grammar School at Bishops Stortford in 1894. In 1938 one was seen at Nomansland Common, south of Wheathampstead. A specimen in the Hopkins/Alexander Collection was obtained at Tring in 1948 and singles were seen near Tring in 1976 and at Tring Park in 1981. One was reported from Tingley Wood near Pirton in 1972 and two were seen at the nearby Knocking Hoe National Nature Reserve, just inside Bedfordshire, on 28 June 1977. There are strong suggestions from the later records that they represent strays from not too distant colonies in Buckinghamshire and Bedfordshire.

By the end of the 19th century the Wood White had become very scarce in the eastern part of Britain and only remained in reasonable numbers in the general areas of the south midlands, the Welsh borders, adjacent parts of Surrey and Sussex, south Somerset, east Devon and in Ireland where a distinct sub-species, *juvernica*, is recognised. Changes and declines in woodland coppice and ride management were partly responsible for this retraction of range, and climate certainly played a major part. Wood White fecundity is significantly reduced by cool wet weather, of which there was much at the latter end of the last century. From about 1970 onwards a slight range expansion has been detected. Some colonies have been deliberately introduced, but some of the more recent conifer plantations with wide flowery rides are facilitating a very gradual spread of this generally rather sedentary slow flying butterfly. The recent records for west Hertfordshire are perhaps precursors of further spread which might lead to the return of Wood White as a resident in our woodlands.

On the wing from late May to July, with sometimes a second generation in August, particularly in warm summers. Wood White is very much a species of woodlands with open sheltered sunny rides and glades. Our smallest 'white', it never rests with its oval-shaped wings open. Quite delicate in appearance, the wings are a rather yellowish-white with a few diffuse darker patches. Males patrol flowery rides and glades with a slow fluttering flight, searching for the more sedentary females. Eggs are laid singly and the larvae feed mainly upon the leaves of Yellow Meadow Vetchling *Lathyrus pratensis* L., although also recorded have been Bitter Vetch *L. montanus* Bernh., Bird's-foot Trefoil *Lotus corniculatus* L. and Tufted Vetch *Vicia cracca* L. Many books, including some recent publications, erroneously list Tuberous Pea *Lathyrus tuberosus* L. and Everlasting Pea *L. sylvestris* L. as foodplants, but both are rather rare in Britain and seldom if ever utilised by the Wood White.


# Clouded Yellow

*Colias croceus* Geoffroy

A. E. Gibbs – before 1826

PLATE
page 62

Clouded Yellow is a migrant butterfly to Britain which, in favourable seasons may breed here. A native of the Mediterranean region it produces continuous generations which, even in winter, require a succession of food plants. Winter generations may expand from the Mediterranean and, throughout spring and summer, breed across Europe, a few, at least, generally reaching southern England in May and June. Largely dependent upon how many arrive here in spring, numbers and the distribution of the Clouded Yellow varies markedly from year to year. Particularly in warm summers, further generations may be produced in southern England, which move further north. Our northern winters preclude survival and most of the later generations

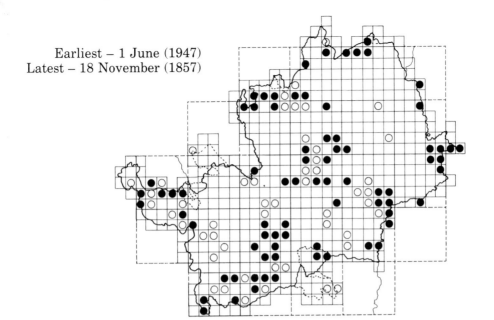

Earliest – 1 June (1947)
Latest – 18 November (1857)

perish, although there are indications that some Clouded Yellows do actually undertake southward movements in autumn.

A. E. Gibbs (1893) wrote of the Clouded Yellow, 'We have no insect in our British fauna more uncertain in its appearance . . . for years it may be sought for in vain, and then comes a season . . . when it may be taken on almost any bright day'. Good Clouded Yellow years for Hertfordshire between the abundance of 1826 and the trickle of 1962, were as follows:

1831 (plentiful); 1835; 1836; 1839 (common); 1843 (abundant); 1844 (very common); 1855 (common); 1856; 1857; 1858 (very common); 1859 (very abundant); 1865; 1868 (common); 1875 (very common); 1876 (common); 1879; 1883; 1884; 1885; 1892 (plentiful); 1900 (in profusion); 1922 (good year); 1928 (good year); 1933; 1938; 1941 (common); 1943 (good year); 1947 (common); 1949 (moderately frequent); 1962 (smallest immigration since the 1930s).

Although in many of the intervening years small numbers of Clouded Yellows were recorded, the uncertainty of their occurrence can be seen. There is no apparent pattern to the frequency and size of these invasions but there has been a definite decline since the turn of the century. The loss of habitats in southern Europe may, perhaps, be a pertinent factor.

For over thirty years it was widely thought that large and widespread invasions of Clouded Yellows were a thing of the past and that in Hertfordshire we would only get the odd one or two, now and then. But in 1983, at least by relatively modern standards, a massive invasion of Britain occurred. Over seventy records were received of sightings in Hertfordshire in that year, relating to probably several hundred butterflies. By comparison, all the other post-1970 records in total relate to just twenty-two sightings. In 1983 Clouded Yellows were seen in the county from mid-June until late October and breeding was confirmed from several sites. A maximum of 200 were seen in

49

lucerne fields at Hilfield Lane north-east of Bushey, including the form *helice* (*see* below), and two broods were produced before the last sighting there on 24 October.

During the Survey singles were observed near Berkhamsted and on the Ayot Way near Wheathampstead in 1984, at East Hyde in 1984 and 1985, and at Whempsted and Oughtonhead near Hitchin in 1986. Although the species tends to have a preference for rough grassland sites, Clouded Yellows could turn up anywhere in the county, the distribution map probably indicating more the areas most frequented by entomologists than areas most frequented by these butterflies.

Clouded Yellows' eggs are laid on a range of leguminous plants including some clovers *Trifolium* spp. and Lucerne *Medicago sativa* L. Throughout Europe such plants are now less commonly cultivated as fodder crops for cattle and it is probable that good invasion years will become even more infrequent. With the exception of Brimstones, Clouded Yellows are the only other bright yellow butterflies likely to be encountered in Hertfordshire. When resting they seldom open their wings, which are more conventionally 'butterfly-shaped' than those of the Brimstone, and it is the underwings that are seen. These are deep yellow with a single black spot near the leading edge of each forewing, and a silver, reddish-ringed figure-of-eight spot centering the hindwings. Upperwings are rich orange with broad black borders and most conspicuous in flight. Females are paler and have a well known form, named *helice* Hübner, in which the orange colouration is replaced with pale grey. During some invasions form *helice* is quite frequent and sometimes outnumbers the more typical form. Quite a number of records relating to *helice* have been made in Hertfordshire. Some claims for sightings of the rare Pale Clouded Yellow (*see* below) and Berger's Clouded Yellow *Colias australis* Ver. as yet not recorded for the county, related to mis-identifications of *helice*.

# Pale Clouded Yellow

*Colias hyale*   Linnaeus

J. H. Grubb – 1873

As noted in the description of the Clouded Yellow, care is necessary in the determination of Pale Clouded Yellows. They are easily confused with the pale form, *helice*, of the female Clouded Yellow, which has been recorded fairly frequently in Hertfordshire, and the, as yet, unrecorded Berger's Clouded Yellow. Unless substantiated by specimens or full descriptions, all Pale Clouded Yellow records must be regarded with a degree of uncertainty. Some of those indicated on the distribution map may be in error.

Since J. H. Grubb published the first county record, of a specimen from Hitchin in 1873, in the *Entomologist* Vol. **8**, p.270, the other most acceptable records are as follows. Gibbs (1893) took several specimens

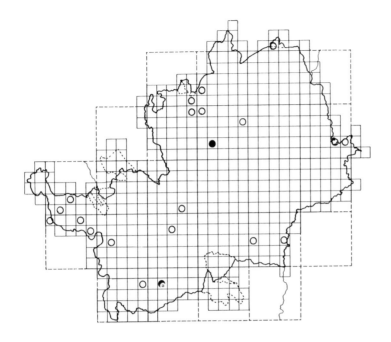

near St Albans in 1877, and a specimen captured by Foster, at Hillend near Langley on 25 July 1892, is still extant in his collections. In August and September of that year, according to Foster, *hyale* and *croceus* 'swarmed everywhere' and the former was 'the commoner of the two'. In 1900, *hyale* was again reported to be more common than *croceus*, even in the streets of towns all over the county. Ten specimens in Foster's collections were taken in that year at or near Hitchin. Further specimens obtained in 1900 from south-west Hertfordshire are in the collections of the Hon. Walter Rothschild at Tring Museum. At St Albans Museum the Hopkins/Alexander Collection has two specimens obtained near Tring in 1901. Five specimens were collected between Bishops Stortford and nearby Farnham, in Essex, in August 1933 and a further Foster specimen, taken by H. E. Smythe, came from the railway bank at Ninesprings, Purwell, near Hitchin in September of the same year. One found dead at Stevenage on 18 September 1976 was given to Peter Waterton (1984) for confirmation. The last reliable record, although not backed up with a specimen, was made at Hilfield Lane during the great Clouded Yellow invasion of 1983.

Both the Pale Clouded Yellow and Berger's Clouded Yellow are very similar to the female form *helice* of the Clouded Yellow and cannot be distinguished in flight. A close examination of the upperwings is essential to separate the three, the most constant characteristics for determination being the dark shading at the bases of the forewings and the markings on the hindwings (Higgins and Riley 1980).

Larvae of Pale Clouded Yellow feed on Lucerne *Medicago sativa* L. and clovers *Trifolium* spp. and in favourable years it is probable that very small numbers breed in Britain.

# Brimstone

*Gonepteryx rhamni* Linnaeus

J. Ransom – 1813

PLATE
page 62
Brimstone has a distinct northern and westerly bias to its distribution in Hertfordshire, related to the presence of those calcareous soils where the main larval foodplant, Purging Buckthorn *Rhamnus catharticus* L. is most frequent. An alternative foodplant, Alder Buckthorn *Frangula alnus* Mill., is found, but only very rarely, in some wet woods in the south of the county and this might support a few small colonies.

Earliest – 14 February (1961)
Latest 10 December (1978)

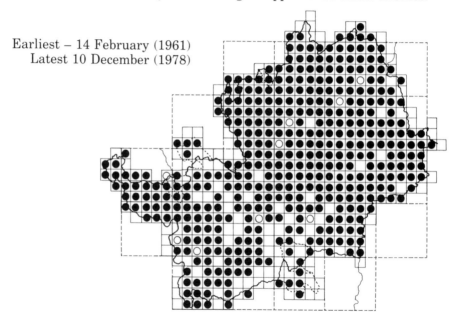

Brimstones are strong fliers, prone to wander, and may turn up anywhere, especially in autumn when they seek nectar-producing flowers to build up reserves for hibernation. Adults are long-lived and can survive for a whole year, although half of this may be in hibernation. It is strongly suspected that many Brimstones travel some distances to secure hibernation sites, notably in woods. In spring a reverse movement occurs back to their breeding areas. This 'minimigration' could be responsible for some of the wide spread of records. There is little to suggest any long term changes in the status of the Brimstone in Hertfordshire, but the expansion of arable farming and the consequent loss of hedges must remove some potential breeding sites.

Brimstones are amongst our most easily identified butterflies. Their colour and angular leaf-shaped wings are remarkable adaptations for hibernation. Hanging amongst bramble, ivy or holly they become practically invisible. In flight the males are most distinctive – their sulphur yellow, 'butter-coloured' wings were probably the inspiration for the coining of the term 'butterfly'. Females are greenish-white and might be confused, in flight, with Large Whites, although the latter have black wing tips. Hibernation ends from late March onwards, with males usually appearing some time before the females. There is only one generation each year and mating occurs soon after emergence from hibernation. Females have a great facility for locating 'buckthorns' for egg-laying and even quite isolated bushes are found. Early eggs are deposited on unopened buds or shoot tips and later ones on the undersides of leaves. No other foodplants are noted in the entomological textbooks, but on 12 June 1986 a female was observed laying eggs close to the tips of leaves, and a few on the stems, of Curled Dock *Rumex crispus* L. at Westmill near Buntingford (T. J. James – personal communication). When I checked the site on the following day I found over twenty eggs. Unfortunately the stand of dock was cut down by the farmer a few days later. A few eggs were found in the aftermath and taken away. Most produced larvae but they would not feed on the Curled Dock provided. This suggests that alternative foodplants may possibly be used.

Larvae are dull green and well camouflaged as they rest on the midribs of buckthorn leaves. Full grown, the larvae generally move away from the foodplant to pupate amongst low growing herbage. There is often an overlap with adults of previous year's generation when emergence of the new generation occurs in July. Both sexes appear together but there will be no mating until the following spring. Before hibernating Brimstones feed avidly on nectar from wayside flowers, such as thistles, teazels and knapweeds, and frequently visit gardens. It is at this time that larger numbers may be seen as they gather at particular clumps of flowers to feed. Although well distributed throughout the countryside, they are usually only encountered in ones or twos. According to the severity, or otherwise, of the season Brimstones may be seen on fine days well into October, and may even break hibernation on mild winter days.

# Black-veined White

*Aporia crataegi*   Linnaeus

Only three records of the attractive, and now nationally extinct Black-veined White have been made in Hertfordshire. One was seen at Whitwell in 1844 and another, seen in the garden at Hailey House, Haileybury, was noted in the Haileybury Natural Science Society's report for 1875. E. W. Nimmy (1921) secured a specimen on 16 June 1918 at Hudnall Common, north-west of Great Gaddesden. A Hemel Hempstead record noted by Foster (1937) is an error of transcription and relates to Nimmy's notes on the Hudnall specimen, published in the *Entomologist*, Vol. **51**, p.258. Of his specimen Nimmy wrote, 'it was in too perfect a condition when captured to have been a migrant'. In the light of detailed research by Pratt (1983) and others, outlined in Heath, Pollard and Thomas (1984), it would appear that the two later records could be the results of releases. It was, and to some extent continues to be, quite common for collectors to gather stocks of the colourful larvae from the continent for captive breeding in Britain. In the early 19th century the Black-veined White was still resident in many southern English counties and in some years quite abundant. By 1900 it was virtually extinct, remaining only in Kent until the mid-1920s. The Whitwell record is the most likely candidate for a genuine free-flying insect that was possibly locally resident.

There have been no apparent changes to the wood edge, hedgerow or orchard habitats of the Black-veined White. Nevertheless the species has become extinct. Pratt (1983) suggests that several factors may have been responsible, including climatically induced disease, agricultural changes and predation by birds.

# Large White

*Pieris brassicae* Linnaeus

J. F. Stephens – 1828

PLATE
page 63 Very mobile, Large Whites are found throughout our towns and countryside from late April to early October, often in considerable numbers. Populations do fluctuate from year to year and have certainly been reduced as pesticides have been applied to control their larval infestations of brassica crops. In 1983 they were widespread and very common, but the first brood of 1984 was very small. Numbers picked up in the second brood and in 1985 there were again many. As with so many other species a very noticeable decline followed the severe drought of 1976. In some years numbers are increased by waves of immigrant Large Whites from the continent. Such invasions are mostly observed in coastal areas but from time to time they are noted at inland places, particularly where their movements become 'channelled' by topographical features. On 7 June 1946, S. B. Hodgson saw a steady westward passage across the hills near Ashridge. He recorded this in his diaries, 'The butterflies closely followed the contours of the ground and there was no settling, dallying or turning aside'. On 7 August 1951 Hodgson observed another immigration and noted, 'hilltop cornfields at Long Green, Berkhamsted were alive with "Whites", chiefly this species [Large White]. Next day there was hardly one to be seen'. The last notable invasion into Hertfordshire was in 1979.

If its larvae were not so damaging to Cabbage, *Brassica* sp. and certain other crops, the Large White might be regarded as one of our most attractive butterflies. Both sexes have contrasting broad black tips to their bright white upper forewings and females are distinguished by two central large black spots on these. Underwings are pale yellow suffused with grey, in bright sunlight the patterning

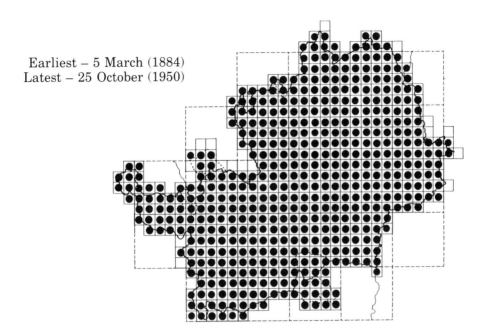

Earliest – 5 March (1884)
Latest – 25 October (1950)

of the upper forewings sometimes showing through. Large Whites are easily separated from the other 'whites' by their larger size, although care needs to be taken to avoid confusion with flying female Brimstones which are similar in size.

After overwintering as pupae Large Whites emerge in late spring, usually around the begining of May. Large batches of eggs are laid on the undersides of leaves of various cultivated *Brassica* spp. including cabbage, brussels sprouts, kale, broccoli and possibly Oil-seed Rape and the garden Nasturtium *Tropaeolum majus* L. A large number were seen apparently emerging from a field of Oil-seed Rape near Hitchin on 13 August 1985. Wild Mignonette *Reseda lutea* L., Weld *R. luteola* L. and some wild cruciferous species have also been found with eggs or larvae. Larvae are gregarious and can wreak havoc in some crops. It is apparent that they are distasteful to birds and the main natural control comes from the parasitic larvae of the 'wasp' *Apanteles glomeratus* L. Eggs of the parasite are laid within the Large White larvae and the parasitic larvae then feed within the host, usually killing it. Sometimes dead or dying caterpillars are found festooned with the small cocoons of the parasite. When full grown Large White larvae move from the foodplants to pupate on walls or tree trunks. A second generation is usually produced in August, and following particularly warm summers a partial third generation may occur in late September and early October. An active larva was found at Watford on 28 January 1885.

# Small White

*Pieris rapae* Linnaeus

J. F. Stephens – 1828

PLATE
page 63

The Hertfordshire distribution and status of the Small White closely matches that of the Large White. In most years it is more abundant than the latter and may be met with almost anywhere, but like many other species it was rather scarce in 1977 following the drought of the previous year. The two or three generations from April to October may be bolstered by continental immigration. Overwintering pupae

Earliest – 9 March (1932)
Latest – 26 October (1985)

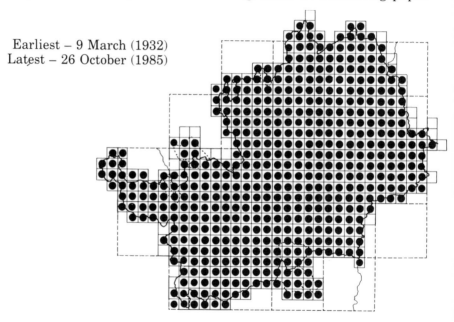

are predated by tits and the first generation is frequently much lower than subsequent ones. Although still ubiquitous and in relatively high numbers Small White populations have been reduced by the effects of pesticides and losses of marginal habitats.

Small White is, perhaps, the most difficult of the three common 'Whites' to identify, especially in flight. It lacks the usually well-defined dark wing-venation of the Green-veined White, and is smaller than the Large White. Also the dark apex to the upper forewing of the Small White is confined to the very tip. Male Small Whites usually have a small dark spot in the centre of the forewing, and females are similar, but with a bolder spot, plus a further spot near the margin of the upper hindwing.

In contrast with the Large White, the eggs of the Small White are laid singly on various species of cultivated brassicas and nasturtium. Wild foodplants include Hedge Mustard *Sisymbrium officinale* (L.) Scop., Garlic Mustard *Alliaria petiolata* (Bieb.) Cavara and Grande, Hoary Cress *Cardaria draba* (L.) Desv. and Wild Mignonette *Reseda lutea* L. Sometimes larvae may reach pest proportions, particularly in sheltered gardens. First generation larvae often pupate on the food-plant, but those of the later generations use walls, tree trunks and shrubs. Here the colour of the pupae closely resembles that of the background.

An interesting habit of several species of butterfly is to seek out moist places during hot dry weather. Small Whites are particularly prone to doing this and S. B. Hodgson relates in his diaries how he counted over sixty together on moist mud by a cattle trough near Berkhamsted Common.

# Green-veined White

*Pieris napi* Linnaeus

Haileybury Natural Science Society – 1873

The Green-veined White is closely related to the Large and Small Whites, but, unlike them, it cannot be regarded as a pest species. Though there is evidence of reduced numbers in Hertfordshire since the days of Gibbs and Foster, due to habitat destruction, it remains widespread and generally numerous but somewhat scarcer on the drier soils of the Chalk, sands and gravels, and in areas of intensive arable cultivation and urbanisation. Preferred habitats are on the damper soils, where it can be found, sometimes in quite large numbers, along woodland rides and margins, hedgerows, road verges, riversides, marshes and damp meadows, in fact almost anywhere that the larval

PLATE
page 59

Earliest – 4 April (1949)
Latest – 12 October (1985)

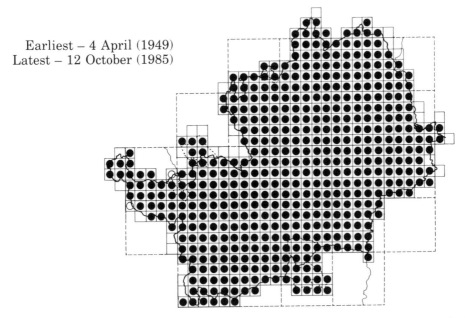

Plate 3   (*Top*)   Dingy Skipper (*Erynnis tages*) [p. 42]
(*Bottom*)   Grizzled Skipper (*Pyrgus malvae*) [p. 43]

Plate 4  (*Top*)   Wood White (*Leptidea sinapsis*) [p. 47]
        (*Bottom*)   Green-veined White (*Pieris napi*) [p. 57]

foodplants grow. Although it has a weak fluttering flight, the Green-veined White is a mobile species and individuals may wander over considerable areas in search of mates, often visiting towns and gardens. Even in the best breeding sites numbers are normally lower than either Large or Small White.

It is quite easy to mistake the Green-veined for the Small White as the two species are similar in size and markings. When airborne its apparently weaker flight pattern may help to distinguish the Green-veined; while at rest with open wings, the Green-veined can be seen to have more extensive dark tips along the upper edge of its forewings. Males have a single black spot in the middle of each forewing and females two, the lower of which may merge into the lower forewing margin. As its name suggests, Green-veined White has a 'green' scaling along the wing veins, which is heavier on the underside of the hindwings and appears green because of their yellow ground colour. The green venation is less pronounced on second generation (summer) females and in some individuals can be almost absent. A good deal of variation occurs within populations of this species throughout Britain and a number of sub-species have been variously described.

Overwintering pupae begin to emerge from mid-April and the first generation are on the wing until mid-June. Eggs are laid on the undersides of leaves of various foodplants including Hedge Mustard *Sisymbrium officinale* (L.) Scop., Hedge Garlic *Alliaria petiolata* (Bieb.) Cavara and Grande, Horse Radish *Armoracia rusticana* Gaertn., Mey and Scherb., Lady's Smock *Cardamine pratensis* L. and Watercress *Nasturtium officinale* R. Br., and have also been found on garden *Aubretia* sp.. Oil-seed Rape *Brassica napus* L. may be particularly attractive in some years, but as yet the Green-veined White is not regarded as a pest of this crop. On 13 August 1983 'thousands' of adults were seen emerging from a field of rape near Hitchin.

Green-veined White larvae feed solely on the leaves, thus avoiding competition with those of the Orange Tip, which share the same habitat and foodplants, but feed almost exclusively on developing seeds and pods. When full grown, larvae forsake the foodplant to pupate in nearby vegetation. Sometimes first generation pupae do not emerge until the following spring, but in most years they produce a second generation which flies in July and August, and in mild autumns a partial third generation may occur in late September.

# Bath White

*Pontia daplidice* Linnaeus

L. Dudley – 1918

Only two reports of the Bath White, a vagrant to Britain, have been made in Hertfordshire. Lesley Dudley, when a pupil at Berkhamsted School, captured the first at the edge of Whippendell Wood near

Chandlers Cross on 27 May 1918. Through Charles Oldham (who recorded the capture in the *Transactions* – Oldham 1921) this specimen, a male, was displayed at a meeting of the Hertfordshire Natural History Society on 26 October of the same year. It is most unfortunate that this specimen no longer apparently survives, for occurrences of Bath White in May, or June, in Britain are rather exceptional. The second record is in Foster (1937) as 'St Albans "one in summer 1921" (Jackson)', with no further details.

It is generally accepted that the Bath White derived its name from a specimen taken near Bath in the 18th century and commemorated by a young lady in a piece of needlework. Although still fairly common in southern and central Europe this butterfly only reaches Britain as a scarce vagrant, mainly in July and August. Occasionally relatively large numbers have been noted, mainly in the coastal areas of the south and east. Such 'Bath White years' were 1872, 1906 and 1945 when some also bred. Unless viewed closely a Bath White might be easily mistaken for a Green-veined White or female Orange Tip. Bath White has white underwings, the hind ones, particularly, blotched with green that is heavier and less broken than that found in the female Orange-Tip. The white forewings of the Bath White are black-spotted at the apex with large central black spots. Bath Whites lay reddish coloured eggs on the flowers, leaves and stems of Wild Mignonette *Reseda lutea* L. and Weld *R. luteola* L.

# Orange Tip

*Anthocharis cardamines*   Linnaeus

Haileybury Natural Science Society – 1873

To many, the first appearance of the delightful male Orange Tip in late April and early May is a most welcome sight, a hopeful harbinger of the longer warmer days of summer to come. Many recorders have noted fluctuations in numbers from year to year and there certainly seem to be fewer noted in recent years as a result of cold wet spring weather. Throughout most of Hertfordshire, however, the Orange Tip remains one of our most common and widespread butterflies. It is less numerous on the drier soils of the Chalk escarpment and the somewhat acid areas of the southern sands and gravels and generally avoids urban areas, while hedgerow removal, the loss and improvement of meadows and neglect of woodlands have significantly reduced numbers, especially in the now largely arable landscape of the north and east of the county. The favoured habitats are unimproved damp pastures, marshes, sunny glades and edges of woodland, and sheltered flowery hedges and road verges. Orange Tip, perhaps in conjunction with some of the other common species, would repay some long-term monitoring studies to assess local population changes in response to developing habitats and climatic variations.

PLATE
page 82

Plate 5 (*Top*) Clouded Yellow (*Colias croceus*) [p. 48]
(*Bottom*) Brimstone (*Gonepteryx rhamni*) [p. 52]

62

Plate 6    (*Top*)    Large White (*Pieris brassicae*) [p. 54]
          (*Bottom*)    Small White (*Pieris rapae*) [p. 56]

63

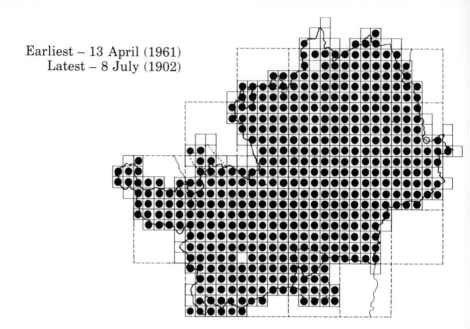

Earliest – 13 April (1961)
Latest – 8 July (1902)

With the bright orange tips to their white upper forewings, the males are easily identified and are on the wing slightly earlier than females. Female Orange Tips are less conspicuous, with dark grey tips and central black spots to the upper forewings, and might, in flight, be mistaken for Small or Green-veined White. Both sexes have beautifully dappled green and white undersides to the hindwings, which provide superb camouflage when they rest amongst the vegetation. Very active, they will emerge for short flights even in periods of fleeting sunshine, seemingly able to predict almost to the second when the sun will appear from behind a cloud. In more settled weather they are quite mobile, the males in particular ranging over wide areas in search of mates. When seen in towns and gardens they are usually just moving through.

Orange Tip eggs, when first laid on flower heads and developing seed pods of various cruciferous plants, are bottle-shaped and white, but soon turn bright orange if fertile – with a close examination of the plants they can quite easily be found. In Hertfordshire the most often selected plant for egg-laying is Garlic Mustard *Alliaria petiolata* (Bieb.) Cavara and Grande, but also recorded are Black Mustard *Brassica nigra* (L.) Koch, Hedge Mustard *Sisymbrium officinale* (L.) Scop., Watercress *Nasturtium officinale* R. Br. and Lady's Smock *Cardamine pratensis* L. The latter plant was formerly quite important for Orange-Tips but has been lost from many areas following the drainage and improvement of damp meadows.

Larval emergence coincides closely with the change from flowers to siliquae (seed capsules). The green larvae are extremely well camouflaged and resemble the siliquae along which they lie and on which they feed. Larger larvae may consume any other eggs or smaller larvae of their own species, but do not compete with Green-veined White larvae which often feed on the leaves of the same foodplants. When full-grown, Orange Tip larvae usually move away from the foodplant to pupate, well hidden amongst thick vegetation, with the pupae resembling dried siliquae of foodplants. Very occasionally, but not known for Hertfordshire, a second generation may emerge in late summer. Any potential female seen at that time of the year should be very closely examined, for it could prove to be a Bath White, which is similarly coloured but with greener under hindwings and more heavily blotched upperwings.

# Green Hairstreak

*Callophrys rubi*  Linnaeus

The Rev. C. M. Perkins – 1878

The distribution map shows that there has been a noticeable decline of Green Hairsteak in Hertfordshire. It does not follow the national trend of being the commonest of the five British 'hairstreaks' although its colouration and frequent reluctance to fly may result in its being easily overlooked and perhaps slightly under-recorded. Perkins (1878) regarded the Green Hairstreak as the 'most common of all this class' and was confident that his readers 'should not fail to find it on the outskirts of Bricket Wood at the end of May, though from its colour resembling the foliage on which it settles it often escapes observation'. There have been no recent reports from this area. Tutt (1896) described this species as 'abundant in Herts', but it has always been rather localised and only really numerous in open Chalk scrub or woods in the Tring–Berkhamsted region and about Hexton. Gibbs (1902) makes reference to Green Hairstreak being 'unusually abundant about the beech woods, both in Herts and Bucks'. Hodgson (1939),

PLATE
page 83

Earliest – 20 April (1946)
Latest – 29 June (1951)

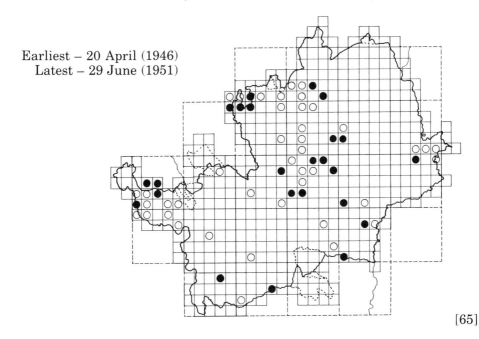

[65]

detailing the same area noted it to be 'fairly common, but local'. In his paper on the butterflies of north Hertfordshire, Foster (1916) considered Green Hairstreak to be 'certainly scarce', but in *The Natural History of the Hitchin Region* (1934), probably as a result of his own later fieldwork, he further describes it as common on the hills near Hexton and abundant at Graveley. 'Fair numbers' were reported from Essendon in 1938 and, in the 1940s, reasonable populations existed in the Knebworth Woods complex, Welwyn, St John's Wood near Walkern and between Thorley and Little Hadham. Elsewhere records are thinly spread, and absent from much of the Boulder Clay and Clay-with-Flints regions. In the past forty years or so many Green Hairstreak sites have been lost through the improvement or ploughing of old grasslands, changes in forestry and the extensive spread of scrub that followed the decline of Rabbits in the 1950s.

Recent records show that small scattered populations of Green Hairstreak remain where suitable habitats still exist, such as unimproved grassland, woodland edges and rides, and railway embankments. Larger colonies may be found on parts of the Chalk escarpment near Tring and Hexton, but even there numbers are not very high and will almost certainly continue to decline as downland and open scrub deteriorate further.

Difficult to see, let alone identify in flight, the Green Hairstreak is, however, easily recognised at rest. It always sits with wings closed, showing the iridescent green, faintly white spotted or streaked, underwings. Except in flight, the dark brown upperwings are seldom seen. In contrast to the other British 'hairstreaks' the 'tails' of this species are reduced to stumps. Green Hairstreaks have a single generation and an extended period of emergence from the overwintering pupae, which lasts from mid-May to the end of June, with some adults still on the wing in late July (there are no July records yet from the county). Colonies are usually rather discrete and composed of a relatively small number of individuals. Males select vantage points on sunlit shrubs from which they make forays to drive off other males and pursue females.

Despite their rather limited distribution Green Hairstreaks are known to use a wide range of plants for egg-laying, depending upon habitat type. On the Chalk, Rockrose *Helianthemum nummularium* (L.) Miller is preferred, whilst on the more acid soils Gorse *Ulex europaeus* L. is most frequently used. Other plants which may be selected include various vetches *Vicia* spp., Bird's-foot and Greater Bird's-foot Trefoils *Lotus corniculatus* L. and *L. uliginosus* Schkuhr., Dogwood *Cornus sanguinea* L., Buckthorn *Rhamnus catharticus* L., Broom *Cytisus scoparius* (L.) Link, brambles *Rubus* spp., and garden *Cotoneaster* spp. Eggs are laid singly on leaf tips or in flower buds, depending upon species. Diurnally active, the green-striped larvae are well camouflaged and difficult to find. Pupation occurs on the ground, often in anthills. The pupae, which can squeak if disturbed, are, like those of many of the 'blues', attractive to ants. It is possible that pupae need to be buried by the ants and that the loss of certain species of ants from sites may be at least partially responsible for Green Hairstreak declines.

# Brown Hairstreak

*Thecla betulae*   Linnaeus

Matthews – before 1896

Brown Hairstreak, now probably the rarest resident Hertfordshire **PLATE** butterfly, was first recorded in the county by a Mr Matthews, of Stev- **page 83** enage, some time prior to 1896. Gibbs (1902) noted that 'it has been taken sparingly in Norton Green Woods . . . about a mile south west of Stevenage'. Bell (1972) reported another observation at the same site on 21 October 1971 by T. W. Gladwin, but, although the area has been well searched, there have been no further sightings. Before the

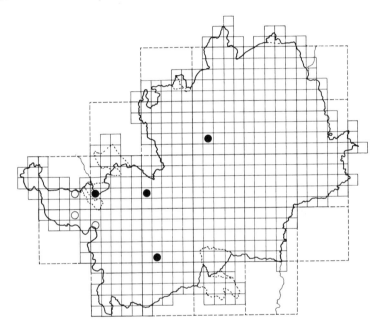

early 1920s Brown Hairstreaks were found 'in plenty' at Long Green, near Berkhamsted (Foster 1937); (Hodgson 1939). Foster (1937) notes that 'two specimens' were taken at Aldbury, 'teste Benson', but gives no date. There were unconfirmed reports, from Plashes and Sawtrees Woods near Barwick between 1969 and 1971, at Rothamsted in 1973, Tingley Wood near Pirton on 13 October 1978, Goldingtons near Hertford on 14 August 1983, and at Clothall near Baldock on 16 October 1986, all of which are doubtful and omitted from the distribution map.

The only really reliable recent records of Brown Hairstreak were made at Hudnall Park near Great Gaddesden in 1983, when a larva was discovered, and at Bricket Wood near Watford (confirmed sighting from the London Natural History Society records). Further information is urgently required on this species and all the above sites should be examined for its presence.

Brown Hairstreak has been lost or become seriously reduced at many of its former haunts in southern England. It only remains fairly common in areas of sheltered hedgerows and woods, on heavy soils, in south Wales, north Devon, parts of Somerset, near Oxford and on the Wealden Clays of Surrey and west Sussex. This butterfly has always been scarce in the eastern part of Britain, but it is a species that may be easily overlooked. Adults emerge in August and September and may fly well into October, spending most of their time amongst the tree tops consuming honeydew secreted by aphids. From a fairly wide catchment area adults may congregate, to court and mate, on a particular tree or group of trees, often an Ash at the edge of a wood. Only egg-laying females descend to the lower growing Blackthorn *Prunus spinosa* L., depositing conspicuous white eggs in a fork or spine base of relatively young twigs. Perhaps one of the best ways of recording Brown Hairstreak is to search for the eggs in winter. During the flight period one needs to be aware that males of a common species of moth, the Vapourer *Orgyia antiqua* L., flies by day along hedgerows and amongst tree tops. This is similar in size and colour to the Brown Hairstreak and can be easily confused with it.

Eggs hatch about the end of April or early May and the bright green larvae feed by night on the leaves of Blackthorn. During the day they rest beneath leaves, exquisitely camouflaged on a silken pad. Fully developed in June, they pupate at ground level in crevices or amongst leaf litter. When they emerge in the following year the adults immediately fly to the tree tops. Both sexes have orange-brown underwings with two delicate white and dark brown streaks running across them and distinct tails. Females are brighter than males. They usually open their wings only in weak sunshine, to reveal a dark brown ground with, on the forewings, faint yellowish patches in the males and large orange bands in the females. In the early 18th century males were known as Brown Hairstreaks and females were called Golden Hairstreaks.

# Purple Hairstreak

*Quercusia quercus*   Linnaeus

Haileybury Natural Science Society – 1873

PLATE
page 86
Despite some losses through woodland clearance and re-afforestation with conifers, Purple Hairstreak remains quite widespread and sometimes locally abundant throughout the semi-natural wooded parts of Hertfordshire. With careful searching this species can occasionally be found in quite isolated oak trees, and is probably under-recorded in several areas. Gibbs (1902) considered it to be 'the most abundant of the Hertfordshire Hairstreaks' and noted beating larvae 'in considerable numbers from young oak trees in Bricket Wood'. Other recorders have shown that Purple Hairstreak is subject to particular years of abundance, most likely associated with fecundity of the previous year

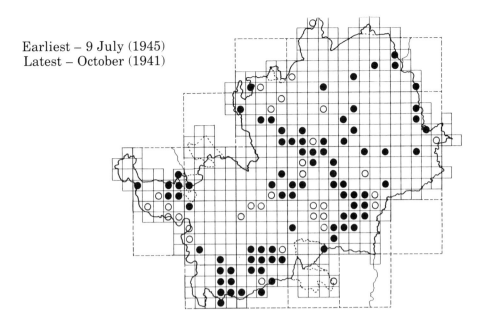

Earliest – 9 July (1945)
Latest – October (1941)

and facilitated by a good summer and the winter survival of pupae, which may be predated in large numbers by birds and small mammals. L. S. Hodson in Foster (1946) noted 'some dozens flying around almost every ash tree' near Essendon in 1945 but 'none was observed around oak'. In 1946 Roger Ferry recorded in his diary 'on aspen – could have taken as many as we wanted at Knebworth Woods'. Such good years still occur and in 1983 Purple Hairstreaks were abundant at Winter-green Wood near Knebworth; many were seen taking moisture from a wet road by Hoddesdon Park Wood, and there were large numbers in the Ashridge woodlands. In other years there is a great paucity with perhaps only a handful of sightings. Although, as noted above, single oaks may support small colonies, most populations are now found in the major blocks of relatively well-wooded countryside and are apparently absent from the arable-dominated regions of the Boulder Clay and Clay-with-Flints. Some individuals are prone to wander and provide casual records. A few recent findings in the north-east of the county suggest that, with further investigation, Purple Hairstreak may be found to be more widespread there, in some isolated woods and copses. The distribution map of this species also provides a good guide to the distribution of ancient semi-natural woodland in Hertfordshire.

As with the other hairstreaks there is but one generation a year. Adult Purple Hairstreaks are on the wing from mid-July to the end of August with a few persisting well into September in most years. The favoured habitat is semi-natural woodland. Overwintering eggs are laid singly on twigs and buds of Common or Pedunculate Oak *Quercus robor* L., Durmast or Sessile Oak *Q. petraea* (Mattuschka) Liebl. and the introduced Turkey Oak *Q. cerris* L. As leaves open in late April larvae hatch and enter the buds, their colouration closely matching the old leaf scales within which they rest during the day, a supporting silken web preventing the scales from falling. At night they feed on the developing oak leaves and, when full grown, may pupate on large branches, but more normally this takes place on the ground amongst moss and litter.

The butterflies spend much of their lives high up in the woodland canopy, sometimes in aggregations possibly associated with a local abundance of honeydew upon which they feed, and which may well not be on oaks. Here they are best observed with the aid of binoculars as they spiral about the tree tops. Occasionally some Purple Hairstreaks may descend during the day, but more are likely to be seen at lower levels on warm summer evenings as they gather ground moisture. At rest the silvery-grey underwings with blackish-shaded white 'hairstreaks' stand out against the summer green leaves. Near the tail is a single black-centred orange eyespot. If they bask, black upperwings are revealed, which turn iridescent purple as they catch the sun. Males have more extensive patches of purple on both fore and hind wings; on the females these are limited to small areas of the forewings.

# White-letter Hairstreak

*Strymonidia w-album* Knoch

B. Piffard – 1882

PLATE
page 86

The distribution map shows that, with the exception of north-east Hertfordshire, White-letter Hairstreak remains in small localised colonies throughout much of the county. It was formerly more widespread and has been lost almost exclusively as a result of the loss of

Earliest – 11 June (1947)
Latest – 2 September (1984)

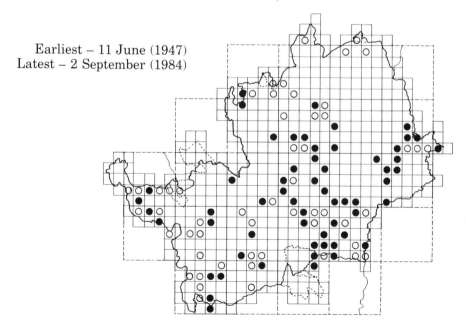

elm trees through the ravages of Dutch elm disease, which swept across the countryside from the 1970s onwards. To some extent this map is also misleading, for there have been a number of extinctions of post-1970 recorded colonies as further elms have died or been removed. In most years a few are still noted and there are indications that breeding is occurring on sapling elms in hedgerows. The current status of this species is somewhat uncertain and difficult to determine for, like all the other hairstreaks, it is often difficult to observe and has probably always been under-recorded. However, as elms continue to die, and as there is no alternative larval foodplant, the White-letter Hairstreak seems doomed to further reductions and local extinctions.

Throughout the Hertfordshire records of White-letter Hairstreak there are many references to notable periods of population increase; in 1882, when Piffard first noted the species for the county he found it 'in thousands near Hemel Hempstead'. Charles Mellows of Bishops Stortford captured 'about two dozen' at Long Meadow near Bury Green in 1900; Hodson (1939) noted the species to be 'abundant on thistles' near Essendon in 1938 and Hodgson described 'a strong colony' at Champneys near Northchurch from 1945 to 1947; Bishops Stortford Natural History Society (1950) reported White-letter Hairstreak to be 'common throughout the district, often abundant' and several entomologists visited the strong colony at Ayot St Peter during the early 1950s. Only a few records were received during the 1984 to 1986 Survey, relating to small numbers. The largest colony found was in 1985 near Walkern, with about twenty individuals; in the following year there were none and the elms had all virtually perished. As noted above, there is considerable concern over the future of this delightful little butterfly, not just in Hertfordshire but in Britain as a whole.

On the wing from mid-July to mid-August, White-letter Hairstreaks spend most of their time high in the tree canopy, resting or taking honeydew from the leaf surfaces of a variety of trees. From time to time they descend, mostly in warm sunny weather, to take nectar from brambles, thistles and privet. Here the characteristic white 'W' marking, which gives this butterfly its name, can be seen on the brown-black under hindwings. The margins of the hindwings have bands of orange and black crescentic markings, and, in fresh specimens, well developed white-tipped black tails. Colonies usually remain quite isolated and localised, perhaps associated with a single breeding tree.

Eggs are laid on or near next year's buds on the twigs of various, usually mature flower-producing, species and sub-species of Elms *Ulmus* spp., most often in a sheltered south-facing aspect. Several of the more recent records of breeding White-letter Hairstreak have been related to Wych Elm *Ulmus glabra* Hudson, which resisted much of the original Dutch elm disease onslaught but is now rapidly succumbing in most areas. In the following spring larvae emerge to feed, at first on flowers and then later on buds and leaves. Pupation normally takes place high in the trees, the dark hairy pupae blending well against the hairy twigs. Interestingly in 1985 five pupae were found on low growing suckering Wych Elm in a thick roadside hedge near Cuffley. This suggests that the species can survive on non-flowering saplings and raises some hopes for its future in the county.

# Black Hairstreak

*Strymonidia pruni* Linnaeus

This species is included on the basis of a letter, from D. A. Tyler of Nuthampstead, published in the September 1970 issue of *Hertfordshire Countryside* stating

> Just before the First World War I captured two Black Hairstreak butterflies on a blackthorn hedge near the now derelict Parsonage Farm at Great Hormead. This was the only time I have seen this variety . . . Having given my collection away some years ago I cannot state definitely the years in which the Black Hairstreak . . . appeared. All my specimens carried labels stating when and where they were found.

The authenticity of these specimens must remain in doubt as Hertfordshire is well outside the documented range of the now nationally rare Black Hairstreak, which is confined mainly to woodlands on the Jurassic rocks and boulder clays between Oxford and Peterborough. Early collectors also often mis-identified and mis-named White-letter Hairstreaks for this species. Attempts were also made in the past to introduce Black Hairstreak to new sites. It is possible that Tyler's specimens may yet be found and authenticated, but until that time the record can not be admitted to the County List.

Interestingly a small colony of Black Hairstreaks was discovered in recent years at an ancient woodland site in west Bedfordshire.

Flying from late June to early July, Black Hairstreak is a rather sedentary species. Even in its strongholds the species is generally restricted to small colonies where good stands of Blackthorn *Prunus spinosa* L. or Wild Plum *P. domestica* L. grow in sunny sheltered situations in glades, rides or margins of ancient woods with a long history of coppice management. Overwintering eggs are laid on the twigs of, usually old, *Prunus* bushes. Hatching occurs in mid-May and the yellow-green larvae feed on young leaves. Pupae are formed on the upper sides of leaves, and resemble bird-droppings – a useful adaptation to avoid avian predation. Adults have golden-brown underwings with a white 'hairstreak' across each wing. The species can be positively differentiated from the much commoner White-letter Hairstreak, which it otherwise resembles, by the presence on the hind wings of an orange border with a row of black spots near the margin. It is doubtful if there will be any significant increase in Black Hairstreak's present range. Being sedentary it is a poor coloniser and its traditional habitat is very much a thing of the past, except in a few woodland nature reserves.

# Small Copper

*Lycaena phlaeas* Linnaeus

Haileybury Natural Science Society – 1873

Over the past forty years or so recorders have noted that Small Copper   PLATE
has declined in numbers and become more restricted throughout Hert-   page 82
fordshire as ancient grasslands have been lost. Populations are
becoming more isolated to small pockets of the more suitable habitats,
a feature which does not show up adequately on the distribution map.
As Waterton (1984) pointed out 'it is widely distributed in rough open

Earliest – 4 April (1980)
Latest – 12 October (1955)

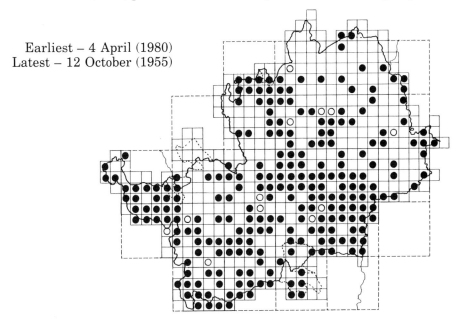

areas' but it is 'unusual to see more than two or three in any one
place', whereas Foster (1934) found Small Copper 'usually abundant'.
In the Survey only small numbers were reported, and the few sites
where any increases were found were restricted to wide verges of
motorways, notably adjacent to some of the bridges along the M1.
Post-1940 habitat changes have been aggravated by the severe
reductions of Rabbits since the 1950s and poor summers of the 1960s,
and these three factors have combined to affect this most attractive
little butterfly quite seriously. The long drought of 1976 desiccated
larval foodplants and Small Copper numbers did not recover to their
earlier levels until about 1982. It remains absent or rare in the intensively cultivated arable regions of the county and most frequent on
open grasslands of the Chalk downs of the west and acid heaths in
the south. Small colonies may be met with in unimproved pastures,
woodland rides, verges, railway embankments, gravel workings and
grassy waste lands, in sunny situations where the vegetation is still
low growing and open. In good summers large numbers are often

encountered, but we no longer get the great numbers that occurred in 1933, when many aberrant specimens were taken.

Difficult to sex in the field, the Small Copper is an active and colourful small butterfly. The black upper hindwings have copper borders and the shining, copper-red upper forewings have black margins and spots. Beneath, the forewings are light orange with black spots and the hindwings brownish-grey. In most years they appear on the wing from mid-May and there are two, sometimes three, broods, with a few adults still to be found in October. They prefer sunny weather and egg-laying is much reduced in cooler cloudy summers. The ball-shaped eggs are easy to find, deposited most often singly, but sometimes in groups, usually on the uppersides of petioles of leaves of sorrels. Common Sorrel *Rumex acetosa* L. in calcareous areas, and Sheep's Sorrel *Rumex acetosella* L. on the more acid soils, are most frequently used, although other *Rumex* spp. are sometimes selected. Feeding larvae create characteristic grooves in the lower epidermis of the leaves. They move from the foodplant to pupate low down in surrounding herbage. Overwintering is in the larval form, from the last generation of the year.

# Large Copper

*Lycaena dispar*   Haworth

In 1945 Mrs Mabel Maynard of Chipperfield wrote to Dr Foster of a male Large Copper seen 'well' by her sister, Miss B. G. Goater, over and on bracken near the pond at Chipperfield Common (letters in the collections of North Hertfordshire Museums). Foster was, quite rightly, very sceptical about this, although no copy of his reply survives and no reference was ever made to it in his reports. Mrs Maynard, obviously more than a little put out by Foster, wrote again in 1946,

> I am quite aware that Large Copper has been extinct for nearly 100 years and my sister also. She so little expected to see one that she had not memorised its appearance and was merely excited and puzzled by what she did see, ... unfortunately I was not there to make sure and my sister did not (perhaps could not because of her paralysis) look at the underwings. ... I hope therefore that you will keep my sister's record in case confirmation should come to hand. If not that – what could an 'All red' butterfly 'smaller than a Tortoiseshell', which after 50 years of observation (and knowing all our major butterflies except the Camberwell Beauty), she had 'never seen before' have been? This letter needs no reply – unless, after you have finished your report, you can suggest an alternative solution. I think I shall not report again for Herts, as we are leaving Chipperfield before long. Perhaps re-introduced butterflies don't count? Yours ....

Foster made no further comment, but filed the letter as requested. Despite Mrs Maynard's remarks, which are reminiscent of some of those still made by a few 'naturalists', particularly in the ornithological world, whose records of rarities are questioned, the description is quite inadequate and remains unacceptable to the County List.

British Large Coppers, ssp. *dispar*, were former, but local, denizens of the fens of Lincolnshire and Cambridgeshire, laying their eggs in July on Great Water Dock *Rumex hydrolapathum* Huds. Their upperwings are brilliantly copper-coloured, the males having two black dots on the forewings and narrow black edges to the hindwings. Females were more conspicuously marked above with black spots and lines. Beneath, both sexes were similar, with blue/grey-bordered reddish forewings and powdered blue/grey hindwings, bearing several white-ringed black spots and black-dotted orange margins. Fen drainage, and possibly collecting, rapidly reduced populations, for by 1860 the British race was extinct. Later several attempts, largely unsuccessful, were made to re-introduce continental sub-species of Large Copper into various parts of Britain. At Wood Walton Fen in Cambridgeshire the Dutch sub-species *batavus* was established in 1927. It still survives there and this site has remained the only place in Britain where this most attractive butterfly can be seen, although its numbers have to be regularly augmented by captive bred stock.

It is just conceivable that Miss Goater saw an escaped specimen, but probably more likely that she mis-identified one or other of our small 'reddish' butterflies, such as Comma, Pearl-bordered or Small Pearl-bordered Fritillary, Small Copper or Wall, all of which might have occurred in the Chipperfield area in 1945. Perhaps a serviceman returning from the battlefields of Europe might have brought back some specimens. The enigma of this record may never be resolved.

# Small Blue

*Cupido minimus*   Fuessly

J. F. Stephens – 1828

Small Blue has always been a rather local butterfly in Hertfordshire, restricted by the availability of the larval foodplant Kidney Vetch *Anthyllis vulneraria* L., which is limited to open, usually disturbed, Chalk soils of downland, pits and cuttings. Significant reductions have occurred in both the distribution and abundance of this, our smallest species. Gibbs (1902) stated that Small Blue was 'particularly abundant at certain spots in the Tring district'. Before 1926 it was 'plentiful' near Watton-at-Stone, probably mainly on the railway embankments there, and 'common near Pirton' in 1946, presumably on the Chalk downs. Before the Second World War a decline was noted by Foster (1934) from 'railway embankments about Hitchin and Letchworth'. Continuing losses of the Small Blue are directly attributable to the disappearance of Kidney Vetch from chalkland sites. Some of these sites have been lost to agriculture, but most have degraded to coarse grasses and scrub as grazing from Sheep and

PLATE
page 87

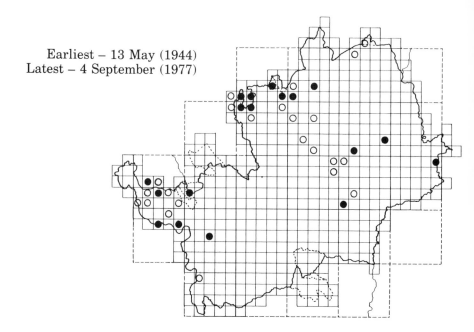

Earliest – 13 May (1944)
Latest – 4 September (1977)

Rabbits has declined. Some Chalk pits have become overgrown or been filled in, and many railway cuttings and embankments have lost their flowery open nature in the years following the withdrawal of steam locomotive services in the 1960s and random summer lineside grass fires caused by stray hot cinders. Very few colonies of Small Blue now survive in the county and they are largely restricted to the Chalk escarpment. The status of these, and more particularly the isolated ones to the east, gives great cause for concern. Numbers are already very low and will continue to decline into local extinctions unless suitable habitat management is forthcoming.

These diminutive 'blues' are on the wing generally from late May to early July, with, in warm summers, a partial second brood in August and early September. Colonies are now usually very small and restricted to discrete, sheltered, sunny situations, perhaps only a few square metres in extent, notably in Chalk pits and on embankments, but sometimes in open areas amongst scrub. Occasionally only one or two plants of Kidney Vetch may support a viable colony. Small Blues are rather inconspicuous butterflies, spending long periods settled on the ground or amongst the vegetation, and may be easily overlooked. Both sexes have dark brown upperwings, the males being lightly powdered with silvery-blue scales. Underwings are pale grey, tinged blue at their bases, with a few white-circled black spots. Pale blue, disc-like eggs are laid on the developing flower buds of Kidney Vetch and, after hatching, the larvae eat their way into the flowers to feed on forming seeds. Later larvae may be more conspicuous as they consume the seed-heads. Full grown, the larvae hibernate in crevices in the ground from mid-summer until about May of the following year, when they pupate.

# Silver-studded Blue

*Plebejus argus*  Linnaeus

Foster (1916), writing of the butterflies found in north Hertfordshire, noted Silver-studded Blue to be 'very rare. Two or three specimens near Hitch 'Wood several years ago. Mr Wightman took a specimen in Letchworth Park about three or four years ago'. He was later (1934) to doubt the validity of these records and wrote, 'probably in error, as it never ranges far from heather' and this species was not included in his County List (1937). Foster's later remark implies that he did not actually examine the specimens and it is just possible that the Silver-studded Blue may have occurred in the county, but, unless corroborating evidence comes to light, Foster's records will remain unacceptable. Heath, Pollard and Thomas (1984) show that old records (mainly pre-1940) have been made not too far outside Hertfordshire, in Cambridgeshire, Essex and the old County of Middlesex.

Since the turn of the century there has been a national decline in numbers and range of Silver-studded Blue. There is a variety of geographical races, regarded by some authorities as sub-species, those of southern Britain being ssp. *argus*, which are found both on acid heathland and on downlands of the Chalk and limestone. Occasionally colonies of ssp. *argus* race cretaceus occur on some southern sites. Although heathers are not essential for the survival of Silver-studded Blue they are important at many sites, and there were certainly some very extensive tracts of heather in Hertfordshire in the past, including the Hitch Wood area, and large areas of Chalk downland on the escarpment from Tring to Royston might have been suitable for this species.

Silver-studded Blue is an extremely sedentary butterfly, living in discrete colonies and usually on the wing from late June to mid-August, although the flight period may vary from year to year. Eggs, which hatch in the following spring, are laid on a variety of mainly woody plants adjacent to short grassland. According to habitat larvae may feed on Ling *Calluna vulgaris* (L.) Hull, Bell Heather *Erica cinerea* L., Cross-leaved Heath *E. tetralix* L., Gorse *Ulex* spp., Bird's-foot Trefoil *Lotus corniculatus* L., Bird's-foot *Ornithopus perpussilus* L. and Rockrose *Helianthemum nummularium* (L.) Mill. Ants *Lasius* spp., as with several of our species of 'blue' butterflies, attend larvae and 'milk' them of secretions produced from their honey glands. Pupation takes place on the ground sometimes within ant nests. Such a relationship, whereby the two different organisms derive benefits, is called symbiosis. The butterfly larvae are protected from certain predators by the attending ants and the ants receive supplies of energy-rich food each time they stimulate larvae. There is still much to be investigated about the nature of these relationships, and several of the 'blues' have been reared in captivity without the presence of ants.

The attractive, and often quite variable, adult Silver-studded Blues derive their name from silvery-blue scales which 'stud' the marginal black spots of pale blue hindwings. Males have violet-blue upperwings with white-fringed black borders. Females are smaller, with varying amounts of orange on the margins of the dark brown wings. They may be confused with the Brown Argus or the brown form of the female Common Blue, and such confusion may account for the early claims for the species in Hertfordshire.

# Brown Argus

*Aricia agestis*   Denis and Schiffermüller

J. F. Stephens – 1828

PLATE
page 87
Except for two sites in the extreme south-east, all other extant locations for Brown Argus in Hertfordshire are based on the Chalk, particularly along the escarpment from Tring to Royston, where the major larval foodplant Rockrose *Helianthemum nummularium* (L.) Mill. occurs. The exceptions being at Broxbournebury Gravel Pit, where a single butterfly was seen in 1980, and Stanstead Abbots

Earliest – 8 May (1945)
Latest – 29 September (1946)

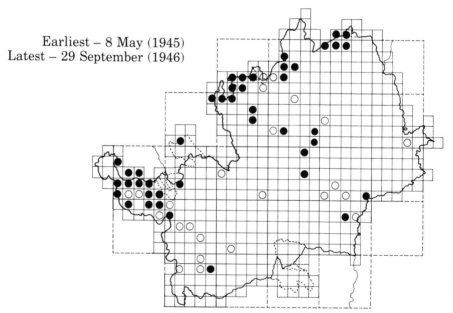

Gravel Pit where a small colony was discovered in 1985. Here, on sandy soils, the larval foodplant is either Cut-leaved Cranesbill *Geranium dissectum* L. or Common Storksbill *Erodium cicutarium* (L.) L'Herit. Local extinctions and reductions in numbers have been noted from many sites in the last fifty years or so. In the early 1970s Brown Argus was seen at Jacott's Hill near Watford, Datchworth, near Knebworth and Hemel Hempstead, but it has not been seen since. Most of these losses are associated with agricultural improvements or the overgrowth of grasslands and railway embankments which shades out Rockrose. On the escarpment only a few places remain where the species can be found, and even at Therfield Heath, the county's largest relict Chalk downland, the population is not large. In his diaries, S. B. Hodgson detailed the loss of a colony from Bourne Gutter near Berkhamsted when the site was ploughed, noted its disappearance from the rough slopes below Berkhamsted Common in 1939 where it was formerly found 'in numbers', and records the very significant decline at Aldbury Nowers after 'the terribly wet summer' of 1954. As with so many other butterflies of the Chalk grassland, reduced grazing following the decline of Rabbits and a series of poor summers are the most likely factors involved in the more recent depletions of Brown Argus populations.

In flight, the colouration of the brown upperwings and blue-grey underwings of the Brown Argus combine to give an impression of silvery-grey, which might lead to confusion with the smaller and rarer Small Blue. At rest, the upperwings of the Brown Argus are seen to be a dark chocolate-brown, with distinctive outer marginal orange spots and a black spot near the centre of each forewing. Brown Argus might also be mistaken for the brown form of female Common Blue or a female Silver-studded Blue.

Overwintering in the larval stage, Brown Argus has two generations each year, the first from mid-May to late June and the second from late July to early September. Eggs are laid singly on the undersides of leaves of the foodplant. Feeding and hibernating larvae are often attended by ants, and pupae are frequently buried in ant hills. (*See* page 77)

# Common Blue

*Polyommatus icarus*   Rottemburg

Haileybury Natural Science Society – 1873

Common Blue is still fairly widespread throughout much of Hertfordshire and remains the most abundant of the 'blue' butterflies. From the reports of several observers there are ample indications of declining numbers. It has become noticeably scarce in, and even absent from, several localities, particularly in regions that are now under intensive arable cultivation. Even on the downlands and heaths there has been a reduction in numbers over the past forty years or so, and few recent records relate to large colonies. Occasionally reasonable numbers may be found in some of the larger recently abandoned gravel workings.

PLATE
page 106

Foster (1937) referred to Common Blue as 'common in all districts' and up to the 1950s the distribution of this attractive butterfly was variously described as, 'usually abundant', 'common in fields and gardens' or 'found everywhere'. S. B. Hodgson's diaries note some of the changes on the downs in the west of the county where, like the

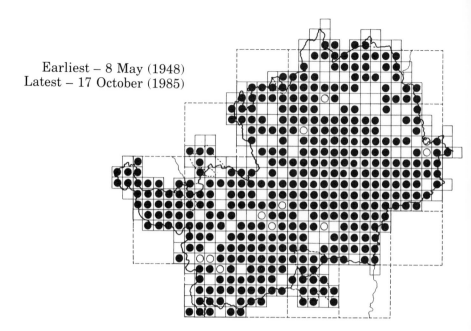

Earliest – 8 May (1948)
Latest – 17 October (1985)

Brown Argus, Common Blue was formerly abundant but, by the 1950s, had become 'comparatively scarce' and was 'hardly ever [found] in sufficient numbers to be worth working'. The disappearance of ancient flowery grasslands through improvement and the expansion of arable agriculture are major contributory factors in the decline of Common Blue. Added to these are further habitat degradations related to the losses of open grasslands, as Rabbits declined and scrub encroached our downland and heaths.

Essentially Common Blue is a rather sedentary species, preferring open sunny short grasslands, and populations are noticeably affected by seasons of extreme climate. Gibbs (1904) witnessed a great decline in the St Albans area in the early years of this century, especially in 1903, the long, cold, wet spell being 'one of the worst seasons on record', and forming part of a rather long period of poor summers. Similar reductions were noted in the late 1950s and early 1960s. The great drought of 1976 desiccated larval foodplants, and for several years after numbers were markedly low.

There are two broods of Common Blue, the first in May and June and the second from late July to September, and in most years there is some overlap between the two. Some individuals from the latter brood may still be seen well into October.

The bright blue males, sometimes with a tinge of mauve or violet on their wings, are unmistakable now that Adonis Blue is extinct in the county. Adonis Blues were a similar but more brilliant blue and, in most specimens, had small but noticeable black markings crossing the white fringes of the wings at the endings of the veins. Female Common Blues can have quite variable upperwings, ranging dark brown to light blue, with orange crescents and outer black spots around the margins. Brown females might be confused with Brown Argus or female Silver-studded Blues. Underwings of males are greyish and females brownish, both having numerous black, white-ringed spots. Aberrations are fairly frequent and best looked for on dull days or in the evenings as they rest on tall grass stems.

Eggs are deposited mainly on the undersides of young leaves or petioles of several species of leguminous plants. In Hertfordshire Bird's-foot Trefoil *Lotus corniculatus* L. on the lighter drier soils, and Greater Bird's-foot Trefoil *L. uliginosus* Schkuhr. on heavier or wetter soils, are most commonly used, although Lesser Yellow Trefoil *Trifolium dubium* Sibth., Black Medick *Medicago lupulina* L. and Restharrow *Ononis repens* L. have been recorded. The pale green larvae feed by day and, as they become fully grown, develop a honey gland which often attracts the attentions of ants. (*See* page 77) Pupation takes place on the ground amongst low growing herbage. Larvae from the second generation enter hibernation and overwinter in the third instar stage. In some years hibernation may commence with larvae from the first generation.

# Chalkhill Blue

*Lysandra coridon* Poda

The Rev. F. H. Knapp – 1856

It is unfortunately apparent that Hertfordshire's only viable popu-   PLATE
lations of the most attractive Chalkhill Blue survive at Therfield   page 107
Heath near Royston and even here the population's future is by no
means certain, for in recent years only small numbers have been
observed. Constant monitoring is essential and, hopefully, with

Earliest – 18 June (1910)
Latest – 11 September (1948)

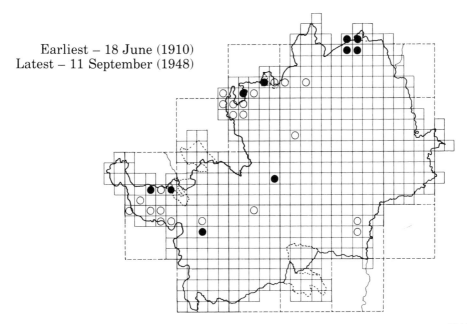

Plate 7  (*Top*)  Small Copper (*Lycaena phlaeas*) [p. 73]
(*Bottom*)  Orange Tip (*Anthocharis cardamines*) [p. 61]

Plate 8 (*Top*) Green Hairstreak (*Callophrys rubi*) [p. 65]
(*Bottom*) Brown Hairstreak (*Thecla betulae*) [p. 67]

83

continuing habitat management directed towards its conservation, the species will survive at this Local Nature Reserve.

Chalkhill Blue is, perhaps, the most famous of Hertfordshire's butterflies, and in the past was extensively collected and written about, since the Rev. F. H. Knapp first reported it from Letchworth in 1856. It used to abound at suitable localities on the Chalk escarpment from Tring to Royston but entered a noticeable decline during the 1920s. Hertfordshire populations were well known to collectors at the turn of the century for their varieties and aberrations. Many collections throughout the country have, or had, extensive series of Chalkhill Blues, many of which were taken at Therfield Heath.

L. Hugh Newman (1967), the well-known broadcaster, author and butterfly farmer, writing in his autobiographical *Living with Butter-flies*, gives some indications of the former status and decline of Chalkhill Blue at Therfield Heath. He wrote

> My father took me with him to Royston, in Hertfordshire, for the Chalkhill Blue season. It is a phenomenon which has never properly been recorded in entomological history that between the two world wars it became fashionable for collectors from all over the British Isles to congregate in certain well-known localities for the sole purpose of searching for varieties of common butterflies. Royston Heath was one of these places, and towards the end of July all the hotels and smaller public houses were fully booked up by entomologists, those who could not afford the expense taking rooms in the town . . . A fashionable meeting place of the time was the Chequers hotel, where collectors would assemble to exhibit their captures and exchange anecdotes.

S. B. Hodgson records in his diaries for 1925–26 that much dealing went on at these assemblies, for 'there was a money market for varieties', and 'competition was absurdly severe and there was much indiscriminate slaughter in haste to examine as many butterflies as possible'.

Newman goes on to describe how he witnessed the beginnings of the dramatic decline of Chalkhill Blue at Therfield Heath:

> During the summer of 1918 you could see these Blues in tens of thousands. This was especially noticeable in the evenings, when they always assembled in sheltered dells and crowded on to tall grasses; . . . four or five often clinging to a single blade of grass. The following season collectors came to Royston as usual and were amazed to find that the numbers of Chalkhill Blues were down to countable hundreds.

Fairly good numbers were still recorded there to the 1930s but the population never recovered anything like its former strength and now only just survives. What long term effects the vast depredations of collectors had, if any, will probably never be known. Several writers have attributed the national decline of this species to various factors associated with ecological isolation, such as increased parasitism, over-predation, poor dispersal potential and 'genetic deterioration'. This last might have been responsible for the apparent increases in varieties and aberrations at several sites and is itself probably caused by inbreeding, as the expansion of arable farming inhibited the movements of these butterflies from colony to colony. Most important was the reduction in Sheep grazing following the First World War and the gradual deterioration of habitat.

Other accounts show the former abundance and subsequent decline of Chalkhill Blue from other downland areas. Gibbs (1894) reported that 'it abounds on Lilley Hoo, near Hitchin', and Cottam (1900) noted 'myriads at Aldbury Downs in 1899, when the whole hillside was grey with it, and up to fifteen could be counted on a single plant of Knap-weed'. First indications of falling numbers at these and other sites were noted in the 1920s. A few still occur at Aldbury Nowers, probably as strays from the adjacent Pitstone Hill in Buckinghamshire, where a good colony remains on the well-managed Sheep-grazed down. No recent sightings have been made in the Hexton and Lilley Hoo area, but small colonies still exist in nearby Bedfordshire on the Barton Hills and Knocking Hoe National Nature Reserves. Apart from at Therfield Heath, the Chalkhill Blue must now be regarded as extinct in all of its former breeding haunts in the county. A small colony did survive on the old railway cutting north of Ickleford but, in 1979, this site was used for domestic refuse dumping and landfilled by the County Council. Odd stragglers, mainly wandering males, have been noted away from the Chalk, but these have become much less frequent in the last twenty years, the latest being seen at Roughdown Common in 1977 and on the Ayot Way near Wheathampstead in 1986.

Along with the problems of ecological isolation, outlined above, two other major factors have combined to cause the reductions of Chalkhill Blue in Hertfordshire and other parts of southern Britain. These are the loss and deterioration of habitat and climatic changes. As has already been mentioned in connection with several other species, considerable areas of short-cropped downland on the Chalk, especially the steep scarp slopes, have been lost. Some have been ploughed as mechanisation has allowed some of the steeper slopes to be cultivated, others have been improved to allow greater productivity from cattle grazing and still others have been lost, from the point of view of their interesting butterflies, through the overgrowth of coarse grasses and scrub as grazing by Sheep and Rabbits has ceased. In consequence, Horseshoe Vetch *Hippocrepis comosa* L., the only larval foodplant, which requires very open usually somewhat disturbed Chalk soils, has gone, as have the 'hill-forming' ants, which are possibly vital to the survival of larvae. (*See* page 77) The loss of grazing Rabbits, which were removed by the ravages of myxomatosis from 1954 onwards, was without doubt a major contributory factor to the decline of Chalkhill Blues.

The full extent of climatic changes is still uncertain but some of the significant variations in Chalkhill Blue populations are at least partially attributable to certain periods of seasonal extremes. For example there were several wet summers at the turn of the century. Droughts of 1921, 1929, 1934 and the early 1940s must have signifi-cantly affected the abundance of Horseshoe Vetch, as did that of 1976. Habitats, as noted above, were disappearing and declining in quality and the series of cool, wet summers of the late 1950s and early 1960s took their final toll on many already ailing colonies of this butterfly.

With just one generation a year, Chalkhill Blues are on the wing during late July and August, a few lingering into September. Discrete colonies can be defined and there may be marked fluctuations in these from year to year. Females are more sedentary than males, often

Plate 9   (*Top*)   Purple Hairstreak (*Quercusia quercus*) [p. 68]
        (*Bottom*)   White-letter Hairstreak (*Strymonidia w-album*) [p. 70]

86

Plate 10 (*Top*)  Small Blue (*Cupido minimus*) [p. 75]
   (*Bottom*)  Brown Argus (*Aricia agestis*) [p. 78]

87

spending long periods low down amongst vegetation. Freshly emerged males have bright silvery-blue upperwings with black outer margins and a series of white-ringed black spots on the hindwings. The white fringes to the wings bear fine black lines marking the ends of the veins. Females are sooty-brown above, often with a bluish suffusion near the bases of the wings, and their white wing fringes are chequered with brown. Hindwings of females may be quite variably spotted, sometimes with marginal white-ringed black spots and occasionally with orange lunules. Underwings are brownish in females, greyer in males, and in both sexes distinctively marked with white-ringed black spots. These variations in the underwing patterns were often highly prized by early collectors.

Single eggs are laid low down on plants of Horseshoe Vetch. Larvae hatch in the following year and feed mainly at night, resting during the day beneath stones or at the bases of the foodplants. Older larvae and pupae of the Chalkhill Blue produce secretions which attract the attention of ants. (*See* page 77). Pupae are usually buried by the ants, an adaptation which facilitates survival during a particularly vulnerable period.

# Adonis Blue

*Lysandra bellargus*   Rottemburg

A. Kingston – before 1896

PLATE
page 106

Alfred Kingston (1896) makes the first reference to Adonis Blue, sometimes formerly referred to as the Clifden Blue, in Hertfordshire, in his descriptions of Therfield Heath

> ... a peculiar characteristic in the butterflies of the Heath is found in the large numbers, in most seasons, of pretty little Lycaenidae, which comprehend those charming little 'Blues' and 'Coppers' with their wonderful tint markings on the wings; but more especially the 'Blues' such as the beautiful little Clifden Blue (*Polyommatus Adonis*) and the larger chalkhill-blue.

The next reference to this species was of specimens taken in 1900 by Arthur Cottam and the Hon. N. Charles Rothschild at Aldbury (Gibbs, 1901). It was however most likely that Adonis Blue had been present in the county for a long time prior to these dates and had, perhaps, escaped detection by its habit of forming quite localised and small colonies. Most unfortunately Adonis Blue is now extinct in Hertfordshire and significantly declining elsewhere. Because of the larval dependence upon Horseshoe Vetch *Hippocrepis comosa* L. its disappearance from the Chalk downlands closely parallels that of the Chalkhill Blue.

In June 1902 these beautiful butterflies were 'plentiful' at Aldbury Nowers, although no second brood was noted and there were no further reports from the area until the 1940s. Foster (1916) found Adonis

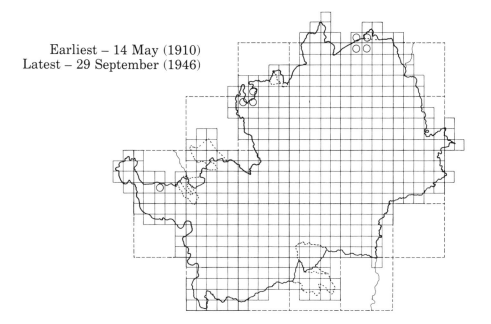

Earliest – 14 May (1910)
Latest – 29 September (1946)

Blues only rarely at Lilley Hoo and on the hills about Hexton and Pegsdon, and thought the species to be 'probably extinct' at Therfield Heath. Here again there were no further sightings before the 1940s. A great resurgence of Adonis Blue occurred for a few years from about 1942 onwards, probably associated with better summers and an increase in Sheep and Rabbit grazing. Several observers reported 'thousands' in both broods near Hexton and Pegsdon from 1943 to 1946. The species was described as 'well established near Tring Station (Aldbury downs) in 1945', by A. L. Goodson of the Natural History Museum at Tring, and Roger Ferry noted in his diary 'a quantity of females at Therfield Heath' on 27 August 1946.

The erratic local nature of Adonis Blue populations is shown by two reports published in the *Entomologist*. Stroyan (1950) notes that, whilst collecting at the western end of Therfield Heath in September 1947, he was astonished to find 'a small colony of *bellargus* in a very small and sheltered "combe" '. He captured and released about a dozen individuals. In 1948 he visited the same location but could find none at all. However, in September of the same year, Bowden (1949) recorded 'more than one hundred'.

There was speculation that colonies of Adonis Blue had been introduced into some sites, although details are difficult to find. Some evidence suggests that a colony was established at Princes Risborough in Buckinghamshire with stock obtained from Folkstone, Kent during the early to mid-1940s. Possible further introductions have also been intimated for the Barton Hills in Bedfordshire, which could account for the apparent sudden appearance of Adonis Blues in the Hexton area, but little firm evidence can be found. It is unlikely that this butterfly could have spread so rapidly to reach Therfield Heath, and most probable that here and elsewhere small populations survived and increased during a relatively short period of optimum climatic and habitat conditions.

The hot dry summers of the early 1940s perhaps facilitated a return of more open conditions on the downs with, at least in places, abundant Horseshoe Vetch. Maybe, with a relaxation of gamekeeping due to the Second World War, Rabbits became locally abundant, creating the very short, disturbed sward beloved by Adonis Blues.

These increases were, however, short-lived and by 1960 Adonis Blue was definitely extinct in Hertfordshire. In his diaries S. B. Hodgson details the decline from the west of the county, where these butterflies were 'locally common on the hills near Aldbury', but disappeared in 1952 when coarse grasses and scrub spread. Interestingly, in September 1950 he also noted that many males were infested with 'red parasites' on the bases of their wings, which may be of significance in some very local reductions in numbers or reproductive capacities, but has little bearing on the major factors causing the overall decline of the species. This has been repeated on a national scale and is associated with the poor summer weather of the period and the loss of open habitat as grazing ceased, particularly when Rabbits were wiped-out by myxomatosis. Coarse grasses, followed by scrub, spread to eliminate bare patches of ground and smother Horseshoe Vetch. Also, collecting may have locally hastened the demise of Adonis Blue; twenty-seven specimens in the Hopkins/Alexander Collection were obtained at Aldbury in 1950, but only two in 1951. A sighting of a single in 1952 was the last record for that area. The last report from the hills near Hexton and Pegsdon was made by Roger Ferry when he collected one specimen on 15 June 1959, and the species was extinct at Therfield Heath before 1959. A record from the old railway cutting north of Ickleford in 1976, noted by Waterton (1984), is unsubstantiated and no longer regarded as acceptable.

Adonis Blues demand sunny, open, sheltered areas, not necessarily extensive, of close-cropped Chalk turf with bare patches and Horseshoe Vetch; suitable sites usually have a south or south-west aspect. They form sometimes very small discrete colonies and have long been known for erratic fluctuations and sudden extinctions. Being rather sedentary their abilities to spread in the contemporary landscape are very slender. As they are at the northern limit of their European range in southern Britain, even subtle climatic and other environmental factors can have dramatic effects upon their numbers.

Adonis Blue has two generations a year. Eggs laid from the second generation in August and early September hatch and the larvae immediately enter hibernation amongst clumps of Horseshoe Vetch. Active again in the following spring, they feed by day, producing secretions which attract the constant attentions of ants. (See page 77.) At night the ants bury the larvae in earth cells, releasing them the following day. Pupae are also tended by ants and have been discovered deep within the ant nests. The first generation of adults are on the wing from mid-May to mid-June. Adonis Blue males have brilliant blue upperwings with, usually, distinct black vein endings crossing the white marginal fringes, a feature not found in male Common Blues with which they might be confused. The less active females are dark brown above, and many are almost identical to female Chalkhill Blues, having small black eyespots within orange and blue (this is white in the Chalkhill Blue) surrounds along the lower margins. They too have white fringes with black vein endings, generally thicker on the forewings. Underwings are greyish in males, brownish in females, with many white-ringed black spots, and are subject to much variation.

As emphasised above, Adonis Blues will only survive in quite specialised habitats. Interestingly the presence of grazing animals may go beyond their controlling the height of the sward, for male Adonis Blues are often attracted to droppings and may acquire essential nutrients from them related to their breeding activities. Eggs are deposited on low growing Horseshoe Vetch, usually in bare places such as tracksides or rabbit scrapes. In late August and early September the second generation emerges, which may contain greater numbers than the first. In some years the second generation may be very scarce or even absent, suggesting survival through to the following year of the first generation. With careful management, certain of our chalkland sites might be made suitable for the controlled re-introduction of this most attractive butterfly.

# Mazarine Blue
## *Cyaniris semiargus* Rottemburg

During the 19th century Mazarine Blue was known to breed sparingly in several limestone districts in Britain, including Bedfordshire, Cambridgeshire and Essex, and even as far north as Yorkshire, but apparently never in Hertfordshire. The last known colony of any size, in Glamorgan, survived until 1877 and, although the reasons are not clear, it is generally accepted that the species was extinct as a resident by 1900. There have been a number of later records attributed to casual migrants or accidental introductions to Britain; Bell (1956) notes that a specimen of Mazarine Blue was captured 'by a schoolboy on the south side of the London Road just south of St Albans on June 11th (1954) (teste C. Ingoldby)'. In the *Entomologists' Record.* **67** No.1 (1955), P. B. M. Allen gave some consideration to the suggestion that the specimen was a continental immigrant and also expressed some suspicions regarding its authenticity. In consequence, unless this specimen or further evidence comes to light, the Mazarine Blue is not admitted to the County List.

Mazarine Blue can easily be confused with the widespread Common Blue. Males of the former species have violet-blue upperwings, narrowly bordered black with white fringes and females are dark brown. Beneath, both sexes are pale grey-brown with a series of white-ringed black spots. Wing bases are tinged bluish and there are no orange spots or lunules. Detailed ecology of the former British populations is not known but larvae do feed on the flowers of Red Clover *Trifolium pratense* L. in flowery meadows of the continent. Some of the casual sightings in Britain may be related to introductions with fodder or seeds.

# Holly Blue

*Celastrina argiolus*  Linnaeus

W. L. Horley – 1870

PLATE
page 107
Although subject to marked population fluctuations and noticeably less common in arable areas of Hertfordshire, the Holly Blue remains fairly numerous and widespread. Several early references note fluctuations. In the 19th century it was apparently scare, but by 1920 it was common. Exceptionally large numbers were reported in 1945 from several locations including Bishops Stortford, Knebworth Great Wood,

Earliest – 12 April (1945)
Latest – 22 September (1902)

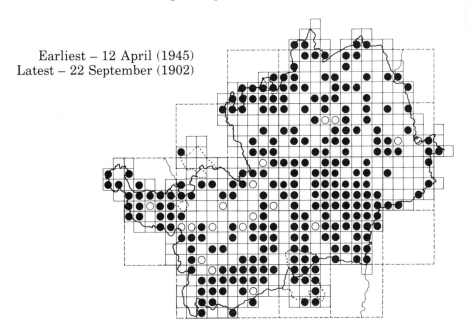

Harpenden and Chipperfield. During the late 1970s a significant decline was apparent, but the results of the 1984 to 1986 Survey indicate that populations are again increasing. Holly Blues are mobile butterflies and colonisation of new areas may happen frequently and suddenly. Perhaps sudden declines may be related to inclement weather or the depredations of parasites. This species would repay further investigations of both its distribution and ecology.

   Holly Blues frequent woodland rides and margins, hedgerows, scrub, urban parks and gardens. There are two generations, on the wing from late April to mid-June and from mid-July to mid-September. Both sexes have lilac-blue upperwings; males have a narrow black margin and a fine chequered fringe to the forewings and might be confused with some of the other 'blues' notably Common Blue; females, although sometimes paler, have distinctive broad blackish borders and white fringes with dark vein endings to their forewings. The black markings are heavier and more extensive in females of the second brood. It is the underwings that are the safest key to identification in the field; they are light silvery-blue with small black dots, unmistakable when seen at rest and giving a silvery look to the butterfly in flight.

Holly Blue is unique amongst British butterflies in its alternation of larval foodplants between the first and second broods. First generation females lay their eggs mainly on the flower buds of Holly *Ilex aquifolium* L. and the larvae feed at night on buds, young leaves and, especially, developing berries. Larvae from eggs laid on the flowers of male Holly trees usually die because they are largely dependant upon the development of berries. Pupation takes place on leaves. Eggs produced by the second generation are laid generally on Ivy *Hedera helix* L. and the resultant larvae feed on buds and developing berries where they can be quite noticeable in causing berries to 'bleed'. A variety of other shrubs have been recorded as larval foodplants, including Dogwood *Cornus sanguinea* L., Spindle *Euonymus europaeus* L., Gorse *Ulex europaeus* L., brambles *Rubus* spp., Raspberry *Rubus idaeus* L. and Snowberry *Symphoricarpos rivularis* Suksdorf. As with many other 'blues' the larvae of Holly Blue are tended by ants. At times, large numbers of larvae may be infested by small parasitic wasps, a factor which may cause some of the notable fluctuations in numbers of this species in certain areas. Overwintering occurs in the pupal stage within a crevice or on the ground. In mild sunny springs emergence may be in early April, a full month before the Common Blue, although in late springs the two species may overlap.

# Large Blue
*Maculinea arion* Linnaeus

British records of the Large Blue, presumed extinct since 1979, have been examined in great detail by Spooner (1963) and Thomas (1984). They highlight a confusing array of mis-identifications, clandestine collection and fraudulent observations. On the basis of these painstaking investigations the only acceptable records are published by Heath, Pollard and Thomas (1984) and come mainly from the West Country, notably north Cornwall and south Devon, the Cotswolds and the Northamptonshire wolds. There are none from Hertfordshire or the adjacent counties, which casts grave doubts on the validity of previously published claims for Large Blue in the county, all of which emanated from Haileybury.

At some time between 1875 and 1888, and noted in the entomological register of the Haileybury Natural Science Society, one Large Blue 'was seen by the College Arms pond' at Hertford Heath. But, this was not the record that appeared in the first edition of the *Fauna and Flora of Haileybury* published in 1888, which related to the fact that there was a specimen in the Society's collections, most probably the 'one specimen shown up for the Cornthwaite Prize some years ago' collected by a pupil, during his summer vacation, and certainly not from Hertfordshire. The Hertford Heath sighting is most dubious and lacks any further substantiation. In the second issue of the *Fauna and Flora of Haileybury* (1902) is a further reference to three Large Blues being seen in 1898 in the Haileybury area. Gibbs (1902) expands this: 'Mr Stockley (a master at Haileybury) informs me that *C. arion* was seen by three collectors in 1898 and that he was within a yard of the specimen', suggesting only one butterfly was involved. It is difficult to understand why such a 'prize' whether it was one or three, was not secured by at least one of these collectors, especially in view of the esteem that would be forthcoming from other contemporary entomologists following such a rare capture. One would have expected that there might be some correspondence or follow-up to the reports from Haileybury but, apart from Gibbs's note, there is apparently nothing. Foster (1937) does not do anything to alleviate the confusion: in fact he made it worse by publishing an amalgam of the records from the *Fauna and Flora of Haileybury* and Gibbs (1902), failing to note that Stockley only referred to one specimen seen by three collectors, not '3 seen in 1898 (Stockley)' as appears in his List. From careful examination of all data, there is no indication of a local specimen of Large Blue ever having been caught and put into the collections at Haileybury. There are four exant specimens of this species in these collections, but all are without any form of data and, like so much of the other material, could have originated from other parts of Britain or Europe. In view of the improbability of these records and the accepted former range of this butterfly, noted above, Large Blue is not admitted to the County List.

Large Blue was not a very mobile species and formed discrete colonies in very short turf on sunny, warm slopes where Wild Thyme *Thymus praecox* Opiz., ssp. *arcticus* (Durand) Jalas and the red ant *Myrmica sabuleti* Meinert flourished together. Extinction was directly related to the loss of this habitat through ploughing, afforestation and the overgrowth of coarse grasses and scrub that followed relaxation or cessation of grazing. Using imported continental stocks, some experimental re-introductions are being carried out at some specially created and managed sites.

Large Blues emerged in late June and early July. Their deep blue upperwings, sometimes tinged purple, had broad brownish-black margins with white fringes and an arching series of black spots on the forewings. Underwings were grey, browner in females, and heavily marked with white-ringed black spots. Eggs were laid singly on the flower buds of Wild Thyme and larvae fed on flowers and developing seeds. After a final moult they fell to the ground at dusk and produced secretions to attract the attentions of red ants. 'Milked' and picked up by the ants, larvae were then transferred to the ant nests where they continued feeding on eggs, grubs and pupae of the ants before entering hibernation. In spring feeding resumed and pupation occurred within the ant nests. Emerging adults crawled their way to the surface to dry and expand their wings.

# Duke of Burgundy

*Hamearis lucina*  Linnaeus

The Rev. G. H. Raynor – 1874

Duke of Burgundy is the sole European representative of the 'metal-
marks' (Nemeobiidae), a pan-tropical family of butterflies. Because of
its colouration, it has a superficial resemblance to a very small 'fritillary' and is often called the Duke of Burgundy Fritillary, although in
size and shape it is more like a 'blue'. Always rare, the Duke of
Burgundy was first reported by the Rev. G. H. Raynor, in Newman

PLATE
page 110

Earliest – 24 April (1957)
   Latest – 7 June (1975)

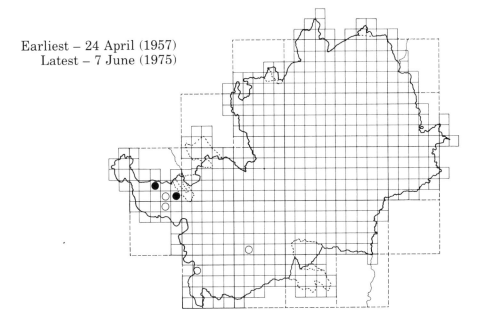

(1874), from Berkhamsted Common. With two exceptions all the other
records related to the Tring–Berkhamsted area. These are noted by
Foster (1937) as 'Bricket Wood 1921 (Nimmy)' and 'Chorleywood in
plenty 1924 (T. Walker)'; no further sightings have been made at
either location. Gibbs (1902) makes reference to Duke of Burgundy at
'Dancer's End, Tring', but this was almost certainly in Buckinghamshire, where the species was not uncommon up to the 1940s.

   This attractive little butterfly was recorded from a small downland
site near Berkhamsted between 1970 and 1979, but has not been seen
there since. This site, now a nature reserve, might well have been the
location of Raynor's 19th century observation. If Duke of Burgundy
has in fact gone from this site, its future in Hertfordshire is in jeop-
ardy, for only very small numbers remain at its other location,
Aldbury Nowers. Foster (1937) indicates that the first reports from
Aldbury Nowers were made in 1922 and it was seen there until 1926.
S. B. Hodgson (1939), who knew the area well, found no evidence of

Duke of Burgundy there between 1929 and 1938, but later noted in his diaries (1957) that a small colony was present from at least 1949, when a 'fresh male with pale forewings was taken on 22nd May'. He further observed that this

> . . . small long-established colony at Aldbury Nowers seems to be extinct after great scarcity in 1957 and 1958. None have been seen since although cowslips and primroses are still fairly common. The butterflies were restricted to the top bank next to the beech wood. They sunned on dead leaves and withered flower heads and were sometimes active over and settling on whitethorn blossom, often disturbing *C. rubi* (Green Hair-streak). They occasionally visited buttercup and milkwort but entirely ignored the beautiful pasque flower which was fairly common.

There were no further records from Aldbury Nowers until 25 May 1971, when small numbers were seen; additional sightings, all of small numbers, followed in 1975, 1977 and 1978.

During the Survey a maximum of five were found there on 30 May 1984, and it is apparent that, although a colony is just about surviving, the future of this species is very much in doubt.

Hertfordshire's loss of the Duke of Burgundy closely parallels the national decline. The species habitat requirements are stringent, being sunny sheltered grassy areas amongst chalk scrub or rides and clearings in certain woods. A sedentary butterfly, it will soon disappear if its breeding sites become too overgrown or shaded and no adjacent habitats are available. Hodgson's description of the abundance of pasque flowers, a rare plant of short chalk turf and now extinct at Aldbury Nowers, is a good guide to what has happened to the habitat there. It is evident that, unless active planned management is undertaken at Aldbury Nowers, Duke of Burgundy will soon be lost.

On the wing from mid-May to early July the small size and colouration of the Duke of Burgundy make it a rather difficult butterfly to observe. Upperwings are dark brown with pale orange patches, black marginal spots and white fringes; on the undersides the forewings are similar but paler; hindwing undersides have two distinct lines of white spots forming concentric bands. Males establish territories in sunny spots amongst open scrub and make rapid darting flights in search of unmated females, inspecting almost any passing insect. Small batches of eggs are laid, most commonly on Cowslip *Primula veris* L., although Primrose *P. vulgaris* Hudson has also been recorded. Before egg-laying the females are extemely selective, taking great care to find larger leaves of flowering plants in just the right situation of sun and shade, before depositing their eggs. Larvae feed at night and, when fully developed, pupate amongst low growing vegetation and leaf litter.

# White Admiral

*Ladoga camilla* Linnaeus

C. Jackson – 1916

White Admiral was not recorded in Hertfordshire before 1916, **PLATE** although it is probable that a few, at least, were present for some **page 110** years prior to that date. Jackson (1921) describes his 'capture' of the first specimen for the county at Symonshyde Great Wood near Sandridge in July 1916 which, presumably to his utter disappointment, escaped and flew off 'whilst being boxed'. This record represents

Earliest – 26 June (1960)
Latest – 30 September (1947)

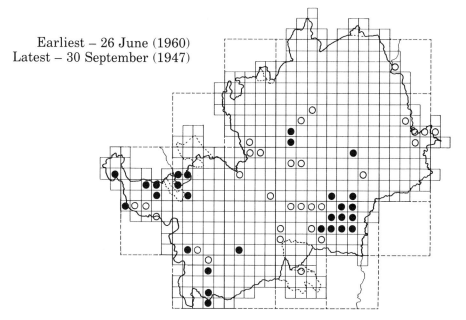

a link in a chain of expansion of the White Admiral noted throughout southern Britain from the early part of this century. In the latter half of the 19th century this woodland butterfly was found only in the extreme south, centred upon Hampshire. Range expansion was rather slow at first, but there was a marked increase in the 1930s and 1940s which is largely attributable to the series of warmer summers and a notable reduction in the amount of woodland coppice management. Suitable areas as far north as Lincolnshire were occupied and, although some significant losses have occurred, there has been little retraction of this national range.

The second Hertfordshire record was not made until July 1933, when a very worn specimen was seen in the Broxbourne Woods. In the following year White Admirals were present there in numbers and in 1935 abundantly. First records were also made in the Tring area in 1935 and by the early 1940s a number of ancient woodlands, particularly those on the drier soils of the south of the county, were colonised. Analysis of records from this period suggests a main wave

97

of colonisation from the south and west, with woods in north and east Hertfordshire being occupied by a westerly spread from sites in Essex, such as Hatfield Forest. The distribution map shows the maximum known extent of this colonisation.

From the mid-1950s to the early 1970s White Admiral became quite scarce in Hertfordshire. This can be related mainly to successions of poor summers that occurred throughout these years. Only small populations remained in a handful of more suitable southern and western sites, notably around Tring and Ashridge, at Bricket Wood and in the Broxbourne Woods. Following the fine warm summers of 1975 and 1976 a sharp increase in numbers was noted at most of these sites, and a subsequent steady range-expansion took place. To date, with the exception of the north-east, a number of former sites have been re-occupied and the indications are that expansion is continuing. Essentially woodland butterflies, White Admirals are, however, strong-winged and will cross open countryside. Given further good summers it is possible that they may turn up in any ancient woodland that has open sunny areas with the larval foodplant, Honeysuckle *Lonicera periclymenum* L. Some conifer plantations with marginal hardwoods and wide rides can also be attractive for White Admiral.

On the wing from late June to mid-August, with a peak in mid-July, the White Admiral has a single generation. A very interesting, perhaps unique, observation was recorded in the 1947 Annual Report of the Haileybury Natural Science Society with 'a second brood out on 30th September 1947 near Hertford Heath'. That year was one of climatic excesses and generally noted as good for butterflies. Winter was very cold, March very wet, and there was summer drought, with August and October being very dry. Such extremes might have stimu- lated the production of a second brood, although it is more likely that the emergence of the first brood was prolonged, perhaps as a result of slow larval development related to a paucity of the foodplant caused by the dry weather.

The White Admiral's rather rounded dark-brown-to-black upper- wings, with a single conspicuous white band, are most distinctive – an aberrant form *nigrina*, lacking the white wing bars, has been seen in Hertfordshire. Males are smaller and rather darker than females but the black spotted and striped, bronze-brown underwings of both sexes make this one of our most attractive species. They can be elusive, often spending long periods in the tree canopy basking or taking aphid honeydew, but they are particularly active on warm sunny days and, in flight, they are among the most elegant of butterflies, with long glides interspersed by rapid soaring and diving around trees and glades. Frequent visits are made to the flowers of brambles *Rubus* spp. and Privet *Ligustrum vulgare* L. for nectar, and they often settle on the ground at damp patches and ruts to take up moisture.

Males establish territories in sunlit rides and glades. After copu- lation the females search for honeysuckle plants in situations of light shade, often deep in the woods. For this reason coppicing, or other woodland management which removes honeysuckle from or around trees, can be detrimental to the survival of White Admirals. The relatively recent neglect of many woodlands has probably been a favourable factor in the spread of this species, although many other species have suffered because of the lack of management. When a suitable location has been found the finely sculptured eggs are laid, usually singly, on the uppersides of leaves. These hatch in August and the small green spiny larvae feed from the leaf margin leaving the midribs conspicuously intact as resting sites. Parasitism can severely reduce numbers of small larvae. During September the larvae are still small, but fold the remains of leaves over with silken cords to form hibernacula. The leaves wither but remain attached to the main plant, protecting larvae throughout the winter. Feeding resumes in the following spring, and when full grown the larvae are bright green with reddish spines. Pupae are curiously shaped, green and purple with a golden sheen above the wing cases and metallic spots in various places. They hang, head down, from leaves and stems of honeysuckle, resembling partially dead, rolled leaves.

Research indicates that warm weather in June, but not drought, is particularly important for White Admiral populations, which are well known for their fluctuations. This speeds up the late larval and pupal stages and reduces predation, thought to be mainly by birds. A series of years with above average mean June temperatures occurred around 1920, 1930, 1940 and from the mid-1970s. These correlate closely with the increase and spread of the species in Hertfordshire. Given good summers in the future, White Admiral may continue to spread, especially if sunny open woodlands with honeysuckle and wide flowery rides and glades are maintained.

# Purple Emperor

## *Apatura iris* Linnaeus

J. F. Stephens – 1833

To many, the sight of the majestic Purple Emperor soaring above the tree tops or creeping 'mouse-like' over the ground in search of moisture from carrion or dung is the epitome of butterfly watching. Very few observers have had this experience in Hertfordshire, but it is still possible in at least one well-wooded area. Unfortunately there are still unscrupulous collectors in Britain and, for the security of this small colony, the precise location must remain confidential.

PLATE
page 111

Stephens (1834) first noted Purple Emperor 'from Hertford in July 1833' but the species remained elusive to many collectors and recorders, including Gibbs (1902), who only knew of Stephens's sighting. Foster, however, collected together a number of 19th century records, which he either passed to Gibbs (1904; 1905) or published himself, (1916; 1934; 1937). During two days in '1878, 1879 or 1880' six were seen flying over the tree tops at Oxbury Wood, on the county border with Essex, near Meesden. In 1882 or 1883 one or two specimens were taken from woods near Walkern; the precise locality was unrecorded, but it was probably St John's Wood, where sightings were

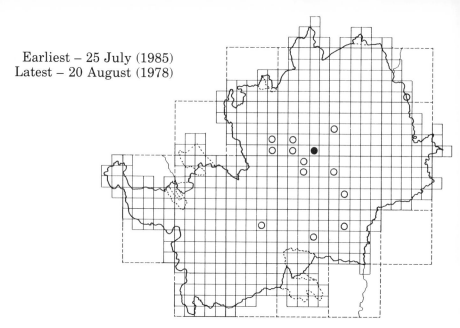

Earliest – 25 July (1985)
Latest – 20 August (1978)

made a few years later. Other late 19th century reports came from
Hitch Wood, Knebworth Great Wood, woods at Mardley Heath and
Welwyn Tunnel Woods (presumably Harmergreen and Lockleys
Woods). Gamekeepers at Knebworth and Welwyn both informed
Foster that 'they not infrequently saw a beautiful purple butterfly
settling on dead birds, rats, etc., hanging in their larders'. Foster also
knew of a specimen, in the collection of the cousin of Samuel Lucas
of Hitchin, taken in Stagenhoe Lane, adjacent to Hitch Wood in the
mid-19th century. In 1896, Foster was driving along the same lane
with his friend, Frank Latchmore, when they saw a male Purple
Emperor settle on some droppings at the side of the road. Hurriedly,
Latchmore stopped the trap and tried to capture the butterfly by
putting his hat over it, but failed.

The first record this century was not made until 1944 when 'one at
Hitch Wood' was reported to Foster (1945), by Harold Course. And
about a year later there were sightings at Cowheath and Brambles
Woods in the Broxbourne Woods complex. Roger Ferry, in his diary,
notes the finding of a pupa in Knebworth Great Wood in 1950. Other
sporadic, but not entirely authenticated, sightings were made over the
next thirty years, mainly in south and central Hertfordshire. These
were from the Oaklands area of St Albans in the 1950s, at Broad
Riding Wood, in the Broxbourne Woods area from 1953 to 1956, with
nine on 28 July 1955, six on 7 August 1956 and an unrecorded number
on 11 August 1956 – the last observation for the area (T. W. Gladwin,
personal communication) Northaw Great Wood in 1962 (James, 1966)
and Astonbury Wood near Stevenage in August 1978. None of these
were accepted by the County Recorders, Bell and Waterton, and
several other entomologists, who regarded the species as extinct in
Hertfordshire, but they may have been a little presumptuous in their
decisions.

On 25 July 1985, during Survey fieldwork, a probable male Purple
Emperor was seen to rise from a pile of chicken feathers near a farm
in a well-wooded part of mid-Hertfordshire. In the same year another

possible sighting was made by a schoolgirl in a village garden about a mile and a half away. Both these records can now be regarded as acceptable, for on 28 July 1986 a male flew into the bedroom of a cottage at the edge of one of the larger woods only a few hundred yards from the first 1985 location. The identity of this specimen was confirmed by the author, who released it and then found another male, on the same day, taking moisture from a nearby track. It is apparent that a small but viable colony of Purple Emperor survives in this part of Hertfordshire, which is probably the only one in the county, and indeed in the whole of eastern England.

Formerly Purple Emperor was found in scattered colonies in areas of ancient woodland across southern England from Devon to Lincolnshire and into Wales. It has now largely disappeared from the west and east of this range, and only remains reasonably easy to find in well-forested parts of west Surrey and Sussex, parts of Hampshire and Wiltshire and at a few sites in Oxfordshire and Buckinghamshire. This decline is closely related to the loss and fragmentation of high forest, and emphasises the conservation importance of the Hertford-shire population. The effects of poor summers are probably also important for larval and pupal development in this species much as they are in the White Admiral, that is, warm weather accelerates early development and fewer larvae and pupae fall prey to birds. There is still much to be discovered about the detailed ecological requirements of the Purple Emperor, and it is quite possible that further colonies of this secretive butterfly may be found in Hertfordshire.

Confined almost exclusively to extensive wooded regions on heavy soils, Purple Emperors fly from mid-July to mid-August and, as they spend long periods in the tree canopy basking or feeding on honeydew, are usually extremely difficult to observe. At times, males, in particular, can be almost absurdly easily seen as they descend to the ground to take moisture, through their bright yellow proboscides, from puddles, wet mud, decaying animal carcases or dung. It is possible to use the last as 'bait' to attract males in some areas, and there are many entomologists who go to considerable lengths to prepare their own 'baits'. The first individual found in 1986 almost certainly 'dropped in' to the cottage garden attracted by dog faeces, before inad-vertently entering the open bedroom window.

The flight of the Purple Emperor is strong, with long glides, the more angular wings assisting in differentiation from high flying White Admirals. Both sexes have dusky upperwings, with patches of white on the forewings and a solid band of white across the hindwings. Under certain sunlit conditions the scales of the males' upperwings refract light to produce the unforgettably beautiful iridescent purple sheen from which the species is named. Underwings show the same markings as the upperwings, on a subtle ground of pink, grey, light brown and silver-grey.

Purple Emperors are known to exist in low densities, covering quite extensive tracts of well-wooded country. On emergence, adults from a fairly wide area will congregate around a particular tree, or group of trees, usually oak (often called the 'master' oak), where courtship and mating takes place – males may often be obvious as they 'battle' for mates. After mating, females disperse into the woods to lay their eggs secretively, singly, on the upper surfaces of leaves of sheltered, partially sunlit sallows, usually *Salix caprea* L., although *S. cinerea* L. has been recorded. Newly hatched larvae feed by night until their first moult, when they enter hibernation attached to the fork of a sallow twig by silken pads. In the following May feeding resumes from resting pads of silk on the upper sides of leaves. Fully grown larvae are bright green with narrow yellow stripes down their flanks and a pair of conspicuous 'horns' at the front. Hanging beneath sallow leaves, the pale green pupae are extremely well camouflaged and difficult to find.

# Red Admiral

*Vanessa atalanta* Linnaeus

Haileybury Natural Science Society – 1873

PLATE
page 130

Red Admirals are the most conspicuous and regular migrant butterflies to Hertfordshire. They prefer wooded areas, but may be encountered in a wide variety of habitats, notably in gardens or on waste land where *Buddleia* spp. grow, and are decidedly less numerous in the regions of intensive arable agriculture. Over the years many recorders have noted significant fluctuations in numbers. No detailed

Earliest – 12 January (1950)
Latest – 29 December (1949)

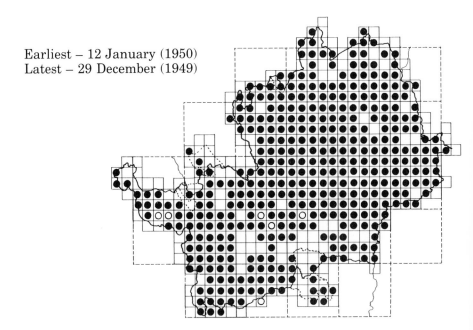

counts have been carried out and there is no evidence to suggest any long term change in the status of this species.

Centred upon the Mediterranean region, Red Admiral populations build up rapidly in the early part of the year and spread northwards, generally reaching Britain in numbers from late May onwards. In flight or at rest they are unmistakable, with velvet black upperwings bearing brilliant red bands across the forewings and along the margins of the hindwings. Towards the tips of the forewings there are conspicuous white spots and in the red bands of the hindwings a series of black spots. Beneath, the forewings are drabber versions of the uppersides, but hindwings are mottled grey, brown and black to give perfect camouflage when roosting. The two sexes are similar and the slightly smaller males establish territories in sheltered sunny places, such as woodland rides, tracks and roadsides. Fertilised females search out sunny situations to lay their eggs, which are deposited singly, mainly on Stinging Nettle *Urtica dioica* L., although Hop *Humulus lupulus* L. and Pellitory-of-the-Wall *Parietina diffusa* Mert. and Koch have been also recorded. Either isolated plants or large stands of these plants may be selected. Recently emerged larvae form feeding tents from leaves folded over and fastened with silken threads. The attractive grey and gold pupae are formed within the final larval tents.

Success of immigrant and local breeding populations is directly related to summer weather, warm sunny years facilitating rapid developments. In good years there are probably two generations in Hertfordshire, with maximum numbers occurring in September and October when they are especially attracted to garden flowers, ivy and rotting fruit. It is thought that most individuals from the last brood attempt to hibernate but succumb in the cold of our winter.

There is a little evidence to suggest that in some years a few individuals may in fact survive hibernation. One was found at Hertford on 29 December 1949 and another at Ashwell on 12 January 1950 – that particular winter was noted for its mildness. Even if a few do over-winter their contribution to the populations of the following year must be marginal. Observations from coastal areas of southern Britain show that there may be some autumn movement back to Europe.

# Painted Lady

*Cynthia cardui* Linnaeus

Haileybury Natural Science Society – 1873

Seldom seen in such prolific numbers as the Red Admiral, the Painted Lady is still a regular and quite widespread migrant into Hertfordshire. In most years a few are noted, but from time to time there are large immigrations and this colourful butterfly may be seen almost

PLATE
page 130

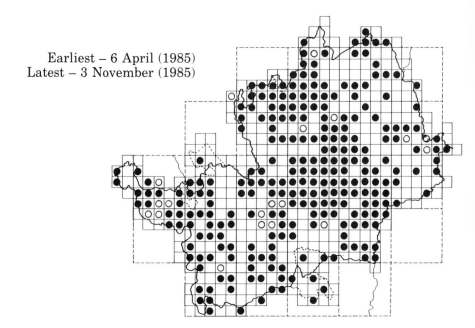

Earliest – 6 April (1985)
Latest – 3 November (1985)

anywhere in the county, especially in sunny gardens and open flowery grasslands. The distribution map is incomplete, highlighting those areas where recording has, over many years, been less intense. In the past little attention was given to the annual fluctuations. Gibbs (1902) describes Painted Lady as 'irregular in its appearance, being very plentiful in some seasons but very scarce in others'. Foster (1937) noted it to be 'recorded from all districts: sometimes common'. Exceptionally large immigrations were recorded in the county in 1892, 1903, 1928, 1943, 1945 to 1949, 1952 and 1980. Recent research (Heath, Pollard and Thomas, 1984) shows that such movements are controlled by weather systems in southern Europe and North Africa. Populations build up rapidly in these regions and begin to disperse, the prevailing weather systems determining the direction and ultimate destinations of the migrants. During the Survey, very few were seen in 1984, a poor year for all migrants, but reasonable numbers occurred in 1985 and 1986.

Painted Ladies generally first arrive here in early June, followed by further arrivals throughout the summer. A few exceptionally early sightings have been made, notably in April 1985, when singles were seen at Therfield Heath and Balls Wood on the 6th and at Kings Langley on the 9th. Further immigration was inhibited in that year by poor summer weather, although some were seen in the autumn. In suitable years, one, possibly two, generations may breed in the county and highest numbers are usually found in August and September. Unlike the Red Admiral, which can survive at freezing point, the Painted Lady is unable to withstand low temperatures. In long mild autumns a few may survive into November, but most are killed by the first onset of frost in late September and October.

Often resting with wings open, a Painted Lady is easily recognised. Upperwings are tawny-orange, although in a freshly emerged specimen there may be a flush of salmon-pink. There are conspicuous white-spotted, black tips to the forewings and a series of black spots parallel to the margins of the hindwings. The undersides of the forewings are paler versions of the uppersides, whilst the under hindwings are a most beautiful admixture of brown, white and grey, with a series of quite conspicuous black, yellow and blue eyespots. On arrival, the slightly smaller males seek sheltered, sunny situations to establish their territories. After courtship and mating, females may range far afield to lay their eggs singly, mainly on thistles *Cirsium* and *Carduus* spp., and – particularly favoured – Musk Thistle *Carduus nutans* L., which is found on the drier calcareous soils. Other larval foodplants are sometimes selected, including Stinging Nettle *Urtica dioica* L., Mallow *Malva* spp., Burdock *Arctium* spp. and Viper's Bugloss *Echium vulgare* L. Utilisation of such plants, which are generally quite widespread and often associated with waste areas, allows this species to colonise sites that are unsuitable for many of our other butterflies. Larvae form feeding webs beneath the leaves of the foodplant, and when they pupate, the grey, gold-embellished pupae are hidden in a similar web.

If numbers build up in late summer, Painted Ladies may be seen, together with Red Admirals, Small Tortoiseshells, Peacocks and Commas, in almost any habitat with nectar-producing flowers. They may be seen still active late in the day when other butterflies have gone to roost. There are reports of both Painted Lady and Red Admiral flying at dusk on warm evenings and some have been attracted to the lights of moth traps.

# [American Painted Lady]

*Cynthia virginiensis* Drury

Of interest, but not substantiated, is the report, made on 12 October 1903 by Lord Aldenham and communicated to Gibbs (1904), of 'four very beautiful insects' seen amongst the abundance of Painted Ladies at his estate, Aldenham Park. Gibbs notes that he thought these might be '*Vanessa hunteri* (= *Cynthia virginiensis*), a North American species which has occurred several times in England. Having no net with him, Lord Aldenham could not capture them'. The North American Painted Lady has indeed been found in Britain, but only as a vagrant from that continent, or possibly from the Canary Islands where it also breeds, having established colonies from the chance arrivals of far-travelled vagrants. Unfortunately, as Gibbs pointed out, 'it is impossible to say with absolute certainty that we have been favoured with a visit from this interesting Nearctic species' and it cannot be accepted on to the County List.

Plate 11 (*Top*)  Common Blue (*Polyommatus icarus*) [p. 79]
  (*Bottom*)   Adonis Blue (*Lysandra bellargus*)) [p. 88]

106

Plate 12 (*Top*)  Chalkhill Blue (*Lysandra coridon*) [p. 81]
(*Bottom*)  Holly Blue (*Celastrina argiolus*) [p. 92]

107

# Small Tortoiseshell

*Aglais urticae*  Linnaeus

Haileybury Natural Science Society – 1873

PLATE
page 131

There is no evidence to suggest any significant long term changes in the status of the Small Tortoiseshell in Hertfordshire. Despite annual fluctuations this familiar butterfly remains quite abundant and widespread throughout the county. It is less numerous, but never the less still frequently encountered, in woodlands and on the edges of open arable lands. In spring and more particularly in autumn Small Tort-

Earliest – 7 January (1940)
Latest – 11 December (1980)

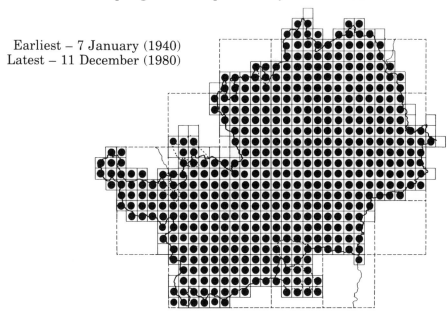

oiseshells are attracted to flowers of parks and gardens. Numbers are normally highest in autumn, especially when warm, frost-free conditions prevail. Hibernation takes place in a wide variety of dark locations, including hollow trees, Rabbit burrows, tunnels, church towers, garages, lofts, outhouses and cool rooms. High levels of mortality may occur in mild wet winters, through predation by other invertebrates, which remain active if temperatures are not too low, and the spread of fungal infections. Such winters are detrimental to most of our butterflies, no matter in which stage they hibernate. Any relatively warm winter's day may briefly break hibernation. Some Small Tortoiseshells, together with Peacocks, that enter houses may be found fluttering against windows when central heating systems are turned on, despite frost and snow outside. These should be gently transferred to a cooler, darker part of the house to await spring.

In most years it is early April before hibernation is really broken. In 1983 a brief sunny spell saw many Small Tortoiseshells on the wing at this time but, before breeding really began, cold wet weather intervened and many perished. This species remained relatively scarce until the summer of 1984. Cold late springs had similar effects in 1985 and 1986 and it was only in the autumns that larger numbers were reported.

Both sexes have orange-red upperwings, with dark borders that accentuate the series of blue crescentic markings of the outer margins. Upper forewings have three black spots across the centre, three black marks near their leading edges, interspersed with pale yellow and a white spot near the apex. Underwings are adaptations for camouflage especially during hibernation; their outer portions are pale buff and the inner areas are almost black. As with many species, male Small Tortoiseshells are active earlier than females, establishing temporary territories near stands of Stinging Nettle *Urtica dioica* L. or Small Nettle *U. urens* L., usually in sunny sheltered locations. Each territory may be occupied for only a few hours before the males move on to new sites. Mating is seldom seen for it takes place deep amongst vegetation. Fertilised females may lay within the territories selected by the males, but often travel some distance until they find situations to their exact requirements. Large batches of eggs may be deposited beneath the terminal leaves of nettles, and young plants are usually selected in more open situations than those chosen by Peacocks, Commas and Red Admirals. Larvae are gregarious until their final instar, spinning conspicuous white silken webs over themselves as mutual protection from predators. Full grown larvae are black, with varying amounts of yellow, and quite spiny. To pupate they may move some distance from the foodplant and form chrysalides on vegetation or walls. Adults that emerge from the spring brood in July produce a second generation, usually in higher numbers, that is on the wing from August onwards. These often range far and wide, notably to gardens, collecting nectar prior to winter hibernation. Small Tortoiseshell has probably always been one of our most common butterflies, its continued success, no doubt, facilitated by the abundance of nettles, which remain common even in arable regions, and the inherent mobility of the species.

# Large Tortoiseshell

*Nymphalis polychloros* Linnaeus

Haileybury Natural Science Society – 1873

Newman (1874) refers to Large Tortoiseshell as being found in 'many localities in Herts', but several later writers show that there was an apparently fairly rapid decline in the last quarter of the 19th century. Gibbs (1902) regretted this loss and lists but ten sites, well distributed throughout the county. He also describes taking many specimens 'twenty years ago – chiefly on the north side of St Albans'. Before the turn of the century there were other reports of declining numbers from Haileybury, Carpenders near Cheshunt and Stevenage. Frank

PLATE
page 111

109

Plate 13 (*Top*)  Duke of Burgundy (*Hamearis lucina*), [p. 95]
(*Bottom*)  White Admiral (*Ladoga camilla*) [p. 97]

110

Plate 14 (*Top*)  Purple Emperor (*Apatura iris*) [p. 99]
    (*Bottom*)  Large Tortoiseshell (*Nymphalis polychloros*) [p. 109]

111

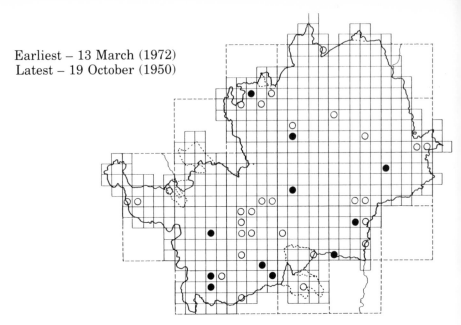

Earliest – 13 March (1972)
Latest – 19 October (1950)

Latchmore of Hitchin wrote to Gibbs, 'formerly this insect was common at Ickleford. The chrysalides were to be seen hanging from the coping of the walls near the church opposite some lime trees. I have not seen a pupa case at that spot for some years'.

From 1902 to 1919 Large Tortoiseshell was only recorded from Stubbings Wood near Tring, New Green Farm now part of St Albans, Bishops Stortford and at Symonshyde Great Wood near Sandridge. In 1920 Charles Mellows found it to be 'not uncommon near Bishops Stortford' and he took larvae, from the 'College Elm' in the grounds of Bishops Stortford College, to rear specimens for his collections. Foster (1934) regarded Large Tortoiseshell as a rarity in the Hitchin region and in his List (1937) only adds two further post-1920 records, from Mymms Park in 1921 and Hitchin in 1935.

By 1940 the Large Tortoiseshell had probably become extinct as a breeding species in Hertfordshire. Subsequent, and many of the earlier, records almost certainly relate to immigrants from the continent. There is also a suspicion that some of the later observations may have resulted from escapes, deliberate introductions or even misidentifications. In 1943 and 1944 singles were seen at Long Meadow near Bury Green and Broxbourne respectively. Specimens were released at Bishops Stortford in 1945 which may account for some, if not all, of the 'several reports' in 1946 from east Hertfordshire noted by Sir John Fryer (1948). There was, however, from 1945 to 1948, a significant national increase in immigrant Large Tortoiseshells and the largest number for this century were reported. Apart from one near Haileybury, no further information is available for those seen in Hertfordshire in 1946. Two were noted in 1948 at Charlton near Hitchin and again at Haileybury.

Between 1950 and 1970 just five reports of Large Tortoiseshells were made, from Odsey near Ashwell (probably in Cambridgeshire), near Hoddesdon, between Buntingford and Standon, near Walkern, and Welwyn. Post-1970 records are fairly widespread throughout the county. Only one location, Pirton, has repeated sightings, with singles in 1978 and 1984, and three in 1982, but there is a suspicion that these may be the results of releases. With the exceptions of two near Burnt Farm, Crews Hill on 13 March 1972 and three at Borehamwood on 21 March 1973, the other sightings were of singles. A dead specimen was found in a shed at Hoddesdon in the autumn of 1976. During the Survey reports were received of one at Pirton in 1984 (noted above) and, a possible, at Rickmansworth in 1985. It is evident that Large Tortoiseshell is no longer resident in Hertfordshire, and probably not in Britain. Livestock is now so readily available from entomological dealers that it is difficult to ascertain whether recent sightings are genuine or not. One was seen by the author at Therfield Heath on 21 April 1987.

It is possible that some claims for Large Tortoiseshells are mis-identified pale Small Tortoiseshells, Commas or even Silver-washed Fritillaries, although similarities are superficial. The wing span of the Large Tortoiseshell is slightly less than that of Silver-washed Fritillary and, usually, considerably greater than Small Tortoiseshell or Comma. Large Tortoiseshells have dull orange upperwings, with the forewings heavily black-spotted, no white patches near their apices and, normally, no blue markings to the black outer margins. Upper hindwings have a small area of black, sometimes obscured by the forewings, and blue crescents, sometimes indistinct, along their black margins. Beneath, the wings are subtly patterned with shades of brown.

In their heyday, Large Tortoiseshells frequented shady lanes and woodland margins. They were very mobile and ranged over wide areas to be seen, usually, in ones and twos. At times colonies would build up in certain places, only to disappear suddenly after a few years for reasons that are still unknown. Some authorities suggest, in expla-nation of this, that Large Tortoiseshell should be regarded purely as a migrant which remains in temporary colonies for a few years after large scale immigration. Others dispute this, maintaining that resi-dent populations were bolstered by the arrival of the migrants. What-ever the reason, the marked decline of this species has not as yet been adequately explained. Widespread disappearance of tall elm trees following Dutch elm disease must be important, although significant reductions in the butterflies were noted before the most recent outbreaks, and larvae have been seen feeding 'in plenty' on low growing elm suckers. Winter survival is, perhaps, of greater import-ance. They can endure the harshest of winters, but damp and mild conditions are likely to result in high mortalities through continued predation and fungal attacks.

Large Tortoiseshells come out of hibernation in early spring to feed on whatever nectar flowers are available, notably the sallow *Salix caprea* L. A series of prolonged winters with cool, late springs could be responsible for eliminating some populations. Eggs are laid in large batches around terminal twigs of, mainly, tall trees. Smooth Elm *Ulmus minor* Miller, English Elm *U. procera* Salisb. and Wych Elm *U. glabra* Hudson are preferred, but larvae have been found feeding on a number of other trees, particularly sallows and willows *Salix* spp. and more rarely Cherry *Prunus avium* L., poplars *Populus* spp. and birches *Betula* spp. Larvae feed communally, resting on webs spun across twigs and leaves. Full grown, they fall to the ground and crawl away to pupate singly on other trees or walls. Adults emerge from July onwards and many feed for only a short period before entering hibernation in hollow trees, log stacks and outbuildings. Some, possibly migrants, may remain active into October.

# Camberwell Beauty

*Nymphalis antiopa*   Linnaeus

J. F. Stephens – 1828

PLATE
page 131

Since Stephens (1828) first noted the Camberwell Beauty from 'Hertford' there have been at least thirty further records of this attractive vagrant in the county. The majority of dated sightings refer to occurrences between late July and October, with just two in spring (both April). The second county record was of one between Watford and St Albans on 12 September 1855. None were seen in 1846 when there

Earliest – 14 April (1946)
Latest – 18 October (1976)

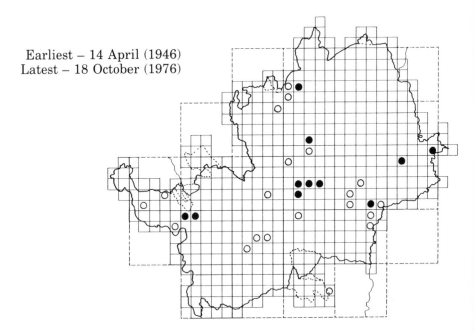

was a large influx in Britain, particularly along parts of the east coast. One was seen at Hitchin in August 1868. Another large influx occurred in the autumn of 1872 and specimens were taken or noted from 'Ashridge Common', Hoddesdon, 'Stanstead' (presumably Stanstead Abbots), at Brickendon Common on 12 and 16 September and Hitchin on 24 and 28 September. Arthur Cottam observed several in the neighbourhood of Hoddesdon in 1875. Other late 19th century reports were made at Hitchin, Southgate and Tring, and these, together with most of those considered so far, were summarised by Gibbs (1902).

In the autumn of 1900 there was an unusually large influx of Camberwell Beauties into Britain, with three seen in Hertfordshire, at Tring during the first week of September, at St Albans on 1 October and near Hatfield on 10 October. These were also noted by Gibbs (1902), who further detailed the St Albans occurrence, an event which adds some poignancy to the sometimes used alternative name for Camberwell Beauty – The Mourning Cloak. This is perhaps best expressed in Gibbs's (1901) own words,

> ... a specimen captured in a class-room at the Hatfield Road Board School, by Mr H. E. Vincer, one of the masters. Unfortunately Mr Vincer has since fallen victim to his love of science, for by a fatal error he drank some silver cyanide which he had prepared for experimental purposes.

Vincer's specimen was exhibited before the members of the Hertfordshire Natural History Society on 26 March 1901 with, no doubt, the appropriate solemnity.

Up to the late 1940s there were eight further reports of Camberwell Beauty, with two at Priory Park, Hitchin, in August 1919, and singles at Berkhamsted pre-1937, Ware on 24 August 1938, Wilbury Road, Letchworth, on 27 July 1941, The Node, Codicote, on 14 April 1946, Wheathampstead in 1946, The Frythe, Welwyn, on 15 April 1948 and Broadway, Letchworth, on 19 August 1948. No other records were made during the next twenty years despite an attempt to establish a colony near Letchworth.

The well known entomologist, broadcaster and butterfly farmer, L. Hugh Newman, in his autobiographical *Living with Butterflies* (1967) relates his life-long interest in the Camberwell Beauty. Following one of his articles in *The Times*, Newman was approached by Mr Norman Jones, managing director of Samuel Jones and Co. Ltd, gummed paper manufacturers of Letchworth, who used this butterfly as their advertising symbol. In the early 1950s the company offered Newman an annual £50 grant, plus travelling expenses, to visit Europe to study the Camberwell Beauty in its native haunts and to investigate the possibilities of introducing it to Britain, not as a publicity exercise for the company but as a worth-while conservation project. Newman expressed considerable doubts about the potential success of such an undertaking but, with the company's backing, began to acquire breeding stock at his butterfly farm in Bexley, Kent.

In June 1958, nearly two hundred pupae, close to hatching, were held at Newman's farm. A meeting was held with the directors of Samuel Jones and Co. and 'it was decided that the well-wooded country surrounding Letchworth might prove an excellent breeding ground, and after studying the Ordnance Survey map of the district a suitable spot was located'. At the end of July, on one of the few sunny days that year, a small group met at Letchworth and went to 'a disused gravel pit which had over the years become an attractive small lake surrounded by willow and sallow bushes. It was a large well-wooded area of several acres and off the beaten track'. Here more than one hundred and fifty Camberwell Beauties were released. The precise location of this site is still uncertain, but it is thought perhaps to have actually been in Bedfordshire, near Arlesey or Henlow. Probably because of subsequent appalling weather not one of these Camberwell Beauties was seen again. This and several other attempts to establish the species in England have all failed.

In the autumn of 1976 there was another large influx of Camberwell Beauty. Parts of the east coast received many from August onwards and in Suffolk there were over three hundred reports. Five, at least, strayed into Hertfordshire, to be seen at Stevenage in August, Bishops Stortford on 20 August, Potten End on 31 August, Tewin on 12 September, Letchworth on 26 September and, the latest ever in the county, at Digswell on 18 October. The only other record is of one on 29 September 1984 settling on apple trees at Hailey Lane, Hertford Heath.

Camberwell Beauty was first obtained in Britain in Arbour Lane, Camberwell, South London, in August 1748, hence its vernacular name. Its native range is from western Europe across temperate Asia and North America, where it frequents lightly wooded country amongst hills and mountains. Most British occurrences come from Scandinavian migrants wind-drifted across the North Sea. A few probably arrive in shipments of timber. It is a most striking butterfly, with unmistakable dark chocolate-brown upperwings, broadly bordered with yellow-cream to white margins and, in most individuals, a series of bright blue spots running inside these margins; cream spots or blotches mark the outer leading edges of the upper forewings. Beneath, the wings are dark sooty-brown with speckled white margins and spots on the leading edges of the forewings. Scanty information suggests that some individuals do overwinter in Britain and that spring records may refer to successful hibernation here. Breeding has never been proven in Britain; probably our climate is too damp, although larval foodplants, sallows and willows *Salix* spp., birches *Betula* spp. and elms *Ulmus* spp., have always been quite common and widespread.

# Peacock

*Inachis io* Linnaeus

Joseph Ransom – 1813

PLATE
page 134

Named from the conspicuous 'peacock' eyespots on the chestnut-red upperwings, the Peacock is one of our most beautiful and easily identified butterflies. It has always been widespread and relatively common throughout southern Britain, and Hertfordshire is no exception. Like all our butterflies, populations of Peacock may fluctuate quite markedly from year to year. Most early recorders simply noted this species

Earliest – 18 January (1983)
Latest – 1 November (1956)

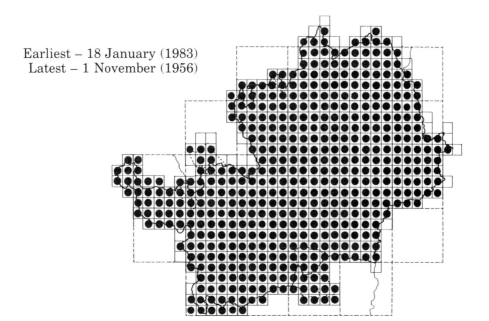

as 'common in all areas', 'recorded from all districts: sometimes common' and 'often plentiful'. Roger Ferry made specific reference in his diary to the abundance of Peacocks at Knebworth Woods in 1946. In recent years when cool late springs have predominated, observers have noted lower than normal numbers in the early part of the year, with a return to more usual numbers in the autumn. Populations are sometimes reinforced by migrants from the continent and the assumption is that there has been little change in the distribution of the Peacock in Hertfordshire since records began, although, as with most species, there has probably been some reduction in numbers from habitat loss, the effects of climatic changes and various aspects of pollution. Together with other common species it might well be considered for some long term population monitoring studies at selected sites throughout the county.

Peacocks are predominantly butterflies of woodland glades and margins. They hibernate mainly in hollow trees, where their grey-black underwings are well-adapted for concealment, and sometimes congregate in large numbers at this time. They may also overwinter in tunnels, caves, Rabbit burrows, outhouses and lofts. Warm sunny days of spring stimulate emergence, usually beginning in late March and April. Very mobile, they range the countryside, and may be seen in any habitat. Males prefer to establish their territories along wood-land rides and margins, hedgerows and lanes. Here they bask, feed and intercept passing females. From about mid-May fertilised females lay large batches of green, ribbed eggs – at times up to five hundred – beneath young leaves of sunlit, sheltered, and usually tall plants of Stinging Nettles *Urtica dioica* L. Hatching in July, the gregarious larvae feed beneath silken webs spun over the nettle leaves. Some-times a long train of larvae can be found as they move from plant to plant. Full grown larvae are spiny, larger and darker than those of the Small Tortoiseshell, and become rather more solitary as they approach pupation. Pupae are formed away from the foodplant, at times high up in trees, and are difficult to find, being greenish-yellow with colourful pink and gold spotted points.

With a single generation, there is a marked gap in June and early July, between those which emerged and died in the spring and the new brood which fly from late July onwards. These may also move about the county taking nectar from late summer flowers, especially Hemp Agrimony *Agrimonia eupatoria* L., Field Scabious *Knautia arvensis* (L.) Coulter, Teasel *Dipsacus fullonum* L. and knapweeds *Centaurea* spp. Flowery gardens and parks are also visited, and large numbers may occur, especially where *Buddleia* spp., *Dahlia* spp., Ice Plant *Sedum spectabile* (L.) cultivars, and Michaelmas Daisy *Aster* spp. are cultivated. By early October most have entered hibernation.

# Comma

*Polygonia c-album*   Linnaeus

J. F. Stephens – before 1813

PLATE
page 134

Over the past two hundred years the Comma has had an interesting history in southern Britain; there have been some very significant changes in its range and status and these have been investigated by Colin Pratt (1986 and personal communication). His references to Hertfordshire are few, but other county data closely follow his detailed investigations and conclusions regarding the national trends of this species. At the end of the 18th century the Comma was found quite commonly throughout much of southern Britain and reasonably

Earliest – 24 February (1985)
Latest – 14 November (1951)

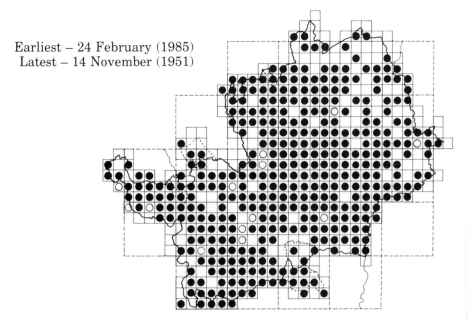

locally up to the Scottish border, but at the beginning of the 19th century it began to decline very noticeably. Stephens (1828) recorded that the Comma had almost disappeared from Hertfordshire before 1813, although prior to that time it had been abundant. Durrant (1888), Gibbs (1902) and Foster (1937) say much the same as Stephens but with errors in the dates. Gibbs (1902) adds two further records, 'reported three or four times near Broxbourne (Stockley)' and 'Mr Arthur Lewis tells me that when a boy he saw (Comma) near the old Cotton Mills at St Albans'. These are unfortunately without precise dates but remain the only other 19th century observations for the county.

From its apparent 18th century abundance the Comma declined very rapidly. Pratt details the overall national decline in the status of the Comma in the first half of the 19th century. There was a notable reduction in the frequency of the species in the south and east by about 1850, but a more dramatic range retraction started from about 1870. At its nadir in 1913 the Comma was more or less restricted to the general region of the lower reaches of the River Severn and northern Clwyd. A few relict populations survived elsewhere in Britain, not in Hertfordshire, and some immigrants were recorded. Some attempts at introductions were also probable, for the species was certainly considered a 'great prize' to contemporary collectors. In 1914 a Comma revival began, which continued until the 1940s, by which time much of the former range had been re-occupied.

On 19 April 1919, C. H. Jackson (1921) took a Comma in Symon-shyde Great Wood near Sandridge, the first county record this century. This relates closely to a slow easterly spread, following a number of good breeding years. Over the next fourteen years about twenty-five further records were made, mainly of singles. Seventy per cent of these were from the south-west portion of the county, the remainder from the Hitchin and Letchworth area. This re-occupation of Hertfordshire was documented by Hodgson (1936) and more than half the reports related to late summer and autumn. Numbers, albeit few, seen at Norton Common, Letchworth, in September 1923 prompted Ray Palmer to suggest a local breeding colony. Breeding was not confirmed until 1933, when a larva was found on nettles by the canal at Boxmoor by Miss A. Lavell.

In 1934 twenty records were made and Comma was regarded as well established but thinly distributed in south-west Hertfordshire, and rare or of irregular occurrence elsewhere. Increases began apace in 1935, and other areas of the county were occupied, including Patmore Heath near Albury and Bishops Stortford. Foster stated that the Comma was 'quite common from 1936' in north Hertfordshire and by the 1940s much of the county was colonised. Fluctuations in numbers were observed; in 1942 it was 'unusually common', in 1945 'quite common', in 1955 'scarce' at Ashridge, in 1960 'unusually common' again and from 1961 to 1966 'not seen' at Northaw Great Wood. An overall general decline in frequency was noted from the 1950s to the mid-1970s. Since 1980 numbers have continued to increase and the Comma was widely recorded in quite good numbers during the Survey except in arable regions.

At all stages in its life cycle the Comma is significantly affected by temperature, and climatic variations are the major influences over both long and short term, national and local, population fluctuations. Long term winter trends are most important, with, as Pratt has shown, increased numbers of Commas following a series of milder winters and decreases following periods of cold winters. Late cold springs also reduce populations. Range contraction and expansion coincide closely with the changes in mean decadal temperatures in Britain. The post-1919 re-occupation of Hertfordshire substantiates this, with winter decadal means being above average from 1910 to 1940, below average from 1960 to 1970 and above average from 1970 to 1985.

Another interesting facet of the Comma, highlighted by Pratt, is that before the turn of this century, it was more or less dependant upon commercial growing of the Hop *Humulus lupulus* L. as the sole foodplant for larvae. At times these larvae were found in pest proportions in some hop fields. Hop growing declined towards the end of the 19th century, except in the warmer, less humid counties adjacent to the Severn Valley. Also insecticidal sprays and other improvements were introduced into hop farming which reduced populations of Comma. There is substantial evidence to suggest that, at its nadir around the turn of the century, the Comma changed from Hop to nettles *Urtica* spp. as the primary foodplant for larvae. It is also possible that changes in agricultural practices, notably the applications of fertilisers, and the dereliction of woods have produced some increases in nettles that have enhanced the spread of the Comma.

It has been shown that the Comma is a mobile species and as such may be seen almost anywhere in Hertfordshire, but it is essentially a butterfly of wooded areas, especially when breeding. Never in great numbers it is scarce, as the distribution map shows, in the arable areas of the county. Identification of this swift flying species is not always easy when it is on the wing, especially the rather golden form called *hutchinsonii* Rob., and it may be, and perhaps frequently is, mistaken for one of the rarer 'fritillaries'. At rest a Comma is unmistakable; its distinctive jagged-margined wings have variegated shades of brown beneath, which, when closed, provide perfect 'dead leaf' camouflage, especially important in hibernation. A white 'comma' mark on the centre of each hindwing gives this butterfly its name. Upperwings are orange (lighter and less ragged in the slightly larger females) blotched with black and brown, and with dark margins. The form *hutchinsonii*, which may occur in about thirty per cent of the adults that emerge in mid-summer, is more golden in appearance and often has less ragged wing margins.

Adults hibernate mainly in woods, often in exposed situations on tree trunks and branches – behaviour which must reduce their chances of survival in cold winters. They are often on the wing earlier in the spring than other hibernating species. Males set up their territories on the margins of woods, in rides and along hedges and sheltered lanes and wait for passing females, which they pursue and court. Eggs are laid in sunny sheltered places, being deposited singly on the leaves of nettles. Wild stands of Hop are also still occasionally used and elms *Ulmus* spp., currants *Ribes* spp. and a number of other plants have been noted. Young larvae resemble bird-droppings for protection from predation and are relatively easy to find on the upper surfaces of leaves. Not so, the beautiful pink-brown, silver and gold pupae which are formed deep within vegetation.

In most years two generations of Comma are found, and in particularly hot summers a third may be produced. A number of adults that emerge in July probably do not move far from their woods and soon enter hibernation. Those that result from the second generation fly in late August and September and may wander far afield, often visiting towns and gardens, to seek nectar from late summer flowers before going into hibernation. In warm autumns individuals may still be active well into November, and on any mild winter's day may temporarily break hibernation.

# Small Pearl-bordered Fritillary

*Boloria selene* Denis and Schiffermüller

The Rev. C. M. Perkins – 1878

Extinct in Hertfordshire since about 1960, the Small Pearl-bordered Fritillary has also virtually disappeared from most of eastern England. It was never very widespread in the county, although at a few sites it was described as 'locally common'. In some areas this species may well have been overlooked or confused with the superficially similar Pearl-bordered Fritillary. Perkins (1878) noted that the Small Pearl-bordered Fritillary could be taken with the Pearl-bordered Fritillary

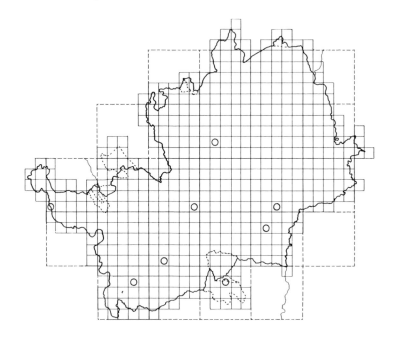

in woods neighbouring Watford in May and June, commenting '*selene* being a little later in appearing and disappearing than its congener – It is astonishing how suddenly these go to bed and disappear suddenly with the sunshine'. Gibbs (1902) detected a reduction in status and recorded 'this insect is not so abundant' as the Pearl-bordered Fritillary, and added only the following mid- to late 19th century sightings – Bricket Wood, 'sparingly' Sandridge (probably Symonshyde Great Wood), Tring, and Norton Green Woods (part of the Knebworth Woods). Foster (1937) adds but two more locations, both from Mr Edelsten, Wormley Woods 'a small colony in 1894' and near Haileybury 'rare', without a date but probably late 19th century.

Only three acceptable Small Pearl-bordered Fritillary records have been made in Hertfordshire this century, all from the south of the county and indicating quite sudden local extinction. A. V. Measday found it still at Bricket Wood in 1949, the Annual Report of the Haileybury Natural Science Society of 1951 notes it to be 'quite common, near Roman Road [Elbow Lane, Hertford Heath]', and A. C. Jackson made the last observation at 'Hadley Woods' about 1960. In the Biological Records Centre at Monks Wood there is a record from 'between Stevenage and Walkern, 1975', but this is considered to be doubtful and has not been accepted.

Too little is known about the ecological requirements of our 'fritillaries', although it is clear that they have all declined very noticeably throughout the past one hundred years or so. The distribution maps show that, all six resident or formerly resident species have fairly similar patterns associated with ancient semi-natural habitats. All were, formerly at least, locally reasonably frequent in sunny open woodlands and grasslands before the general historic character of the countryside was changed through cessation of coppicing, reafforestation, spread of arable cultivation, large scale land-drainage, overgrowth and improvement of grasslands, urbanisation and the widespread fragmentation and isolation of habitats. Each species has its own requirements and tolerances to ecological changes, but all the fritillaries have very seriously declined or become extinct, not just in Hertfordshire but in much of eastern England.

Close examination of Small Pearl-bordered Fritillary records show that it was only found very locally, sometimes in good numbers, in wetter open woods and scrubby commons, with adjacent damp meadows or rough grazings, where violets were abundant. It was never, as far as can be ascertained, in the woods and copses on the colder soils of the Boulder Clay. Its decline can be related to the increased shading of woods as coppicing ceased and to the natural regeneration of trees and shrubs on commons and rough pastures when general cutting and grazing were withdrawn. Cultivation, improvement and drainage of adjacent grasslands accentuated the decline. The few colonies that continued into this century were probably too small and isolated to survive in the changed landscape, and finally succumbed to the poor weather and reduced grazing, even in woods, following the reduction in Rabbits, in the late 1950s and early 1960s.

As Perkins so eloquently noted (above), Small Pearl-bordered Fritillaries are on the wing from the very end of May until the beginning of July, rather later than the Pearl-bordered Fritillary, but with some overlap. They are the smallest of our woodland fritillaries, being slightly smaller than Gatekeepers. Upperwings are deep orange with a series of black veins, wavy lines, spots and crescents and white, black-spotted margins. Females are slightly larger and tend to be of a lighter shade, but both sexes appear darker than Pearl-bordered Fritillaries. All our orange-upperwinged fritillaries might, at a cursory glance, be difficult to distinguish and could be confused with some of the superficially similar, more common, butterflies such as Comma and Wall. Underwings are, however, quite distinctive in most of the fritillaries. Small Pearl-bordered has a variegated pattern of red-brown and pale yellow, with a series of seven silver 'pearls' around the margins and six or seven further 'pearl' markings close to the bases of the hindwings.

Small Pearl-bordered Fritillaries form small discrete colonies. On warm sunny days males actively skim low to the ground in open areas searching for the more secretive females. Eggs are laid, or dropped, on or close to the leaves of clumps of Common Dog Violet *Viola riviniana* Rchb. growing in open sunny situations. Young larvae feed on the violet's leaves until half grown, when they enter hibernation beneath dead leaf litter. In the following spring feeding resumes between intermittent long periods of rest amongst leaf litter. Pupation takes place amongst surrounding vegetation, the silver-pointed dark brown chrysalides being extremely well camouflaged and difficult to find. In some very warm summers a few larvae may continue to feed until full grown and produce a small partial second brood in August.

# Pearl-bordered Fritillary

*Boloria euphrosyne*   Linnaeus

A. E. Gibbs – c 1860

This butterfly, which is easily confused with the Small Pearl-bordered Fritillary, is also now regarded as extinct as a breeding species in Hertfordshire. It is thought, however, that a small colony still exists just outside the county border with Buckinghamshire, near Pitstone, and the odd wanderer may stray across or, hopefully, recolonisation occur. Records show that Pearl-bordered Fritillary was considerably more frequent and numerous than the Small Pearl-bordered Fritillary. It had a slightly more widespread distribution within former areas of open woodlands and lightly tree-ed commons on the drier chalk and gravel soils. Very few records come from the Boulder Clay woods in the north-east portion of the county, perhaps indicating that these were too wet or overgrown even in the 19th century. Pearl-bordered Fritillary was first reported from 'woods near Ashridge' about 1860 and Gibbs (1902) says 'this, the most abundant of the Hertfordshire fritillaries, often flies in considerable numbers in woodlands in May

PLATE
page 135

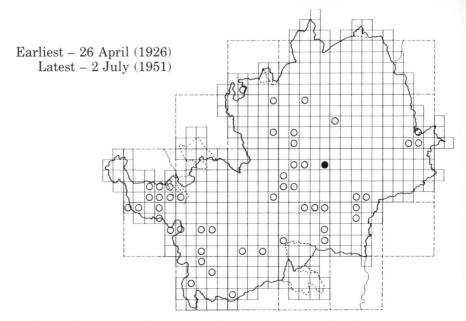

Earliest – 26 April (1926)
Latest – 2 July (1951)

and June'. Most of the reports for this species related to discrete, formerly open, woodland complexes with adjacent unimproved grasslands, and in several localities it remained locally 'common' until the mid-1950s.

Annual Reports of the Haileybury Natural Science Society for 1873 and 1923 listed Pearl-bordered Fritillary for the Haileybury area; the 1949 report recorded it as 'fairly abundant, Roman Road' and a manuscript dated about 1950 by M. Godfrey, a pupil at Haileybury College, notes that the species 'abounds in Goldings Wood, surrounding meadows and Hertford Heath'. In the nearby Broxbourne Woods there were observations made in 1939 and 1948, but no indications regarding numbers. Gibbs took specimens at Bricket Wood on 2 June 1883, and there is a specimen from this locality, dated 1895, in the collections of North Hertfordshire Museums. It was apparently never numerous at Bricket Wood but remained there until 1956. In 1893 sightings or captures were made at Ayot, Brocket Park and Symonshyde Great Wood; specimens in St Albans Museum show that it was still present in the latter locality from 1949 to 1958. Also in 1893 came the first reports from Hitch Wood where Gatward and Latchmore found it 'in numbers', and, Foster (1916) described it as 'comparatively abundant', but there are no further records assignable to this location.

At 'Norton Green Woods' (part of the Knebworth Woods) Pearl-bordered Fritillaries were reported to Gibbs (1902) to be 'common' in the late 19th century, although Foster (1916) had only seen it once. Many were seen in the same area, at Newton Wood, on 18 May 1921 by S. R. Bowden. More records were made in the Knebworth Woods complex from 1922 to 1947 but no indication of abundance is given. In 1948 Roger Ferry took eighteen specimens there for his collection, now housed at Welwyn–Hatfield Museum. His notebook for 1951 states 'common at Knebworth Great Wood'. The last sighting for this area was made by the Letchworth Naturalists' Society (1953), when 'plenty' were observed on 10 June 1951, which gives an indication of how rapidly this butterfly declined from some of its former sites, for despite annual visits to Knebworth Woods, the Society could find no further trace.

Information in the diaries of S. B. Hodgson shows that Pearl-bordered Fritillary was 'fairly common throughout the Ashridge Woods and adjoining commons' prior to the 1940s. From 1948 to 1958 'it occurred in some numbers' within new clearings on the north side of Hockeridge Wood on the county border just south of Berkhamsted. A few were found in 1950 and 1951 on a 'rough bushy slope of a former larch wood in Bourne Gutter' near Bovingdon. At Aldbury Nowers it was 'fairly common' in the wood from 1950 to 1956 but subsequently it 'unaccountably disappeared', although Arthur Measday recorded it there in 1961, perhaps as a stray from Buckinghamshire. The last reports from this western part of Hertfordshire are found in the files of the Biological Records Centre at Monks Wood and the collections at St Albans Museum, with sightings at Great Gaddesden in 1957, Ashridge Park in 1957 and 1959 and specimens from near Tring taken between 1947 and 1961.

In the southern part of the county records of Pearl-bordered Fritillary are few and scattered. Gibbs (1902) notes it from Oxhey Wood and Watford, and Foster (1937) adds Mymms, Northaw, near Radlett and Chorleywood. Several specimens in the B. Turnpenny Collection, at North Hertfordshire Museums, were taken at South Mimms in 1945, and in the same year records were made at Chipperfield and Commonwood Commons. From 1948 to 1956 it was known at Whippendell Woods near Watford, although the size of the colony was not documented.

In central Hertfordshire Ray Palmer found a worn specimen at Harmergreen Wood on 13 June 1926, and in 1936 it was recorded at Sherrardspark Wood, Welwyn Garden City. A few specimens were obtained at Essendon from 1943 to 1945, where, in 1945, L. S. Hodson described it as being 'in some numbers at The Roughs and Furze Wood, – although cut and ploughed'. In 1961 Pearl-bordered Fritillary turned up near Digswell and from 1972 to 1978 a small colony, the last in the county, was known adjacent to wide rides in the Forestry Commission woodlands at Brights Hill near Bramfield.

In the northern and eastern parts of Hertfordshire very few records of Pearl-bordered Fritillary have been made. Gibbs (1902) noted it for the Bishops Stortford area, and from about 1940 to 1956 small numbers were found at Long Meadow near Bury Green, just west of the town and perhaps the site of the earlier report. Two larvae were discovered in the nearby Bloodhounds Wood in 1945. Also in 1945 it was reported as 'numerous' at St John's Wood near Walkern and seen again there in 1948. Foster (1937) located it at Graveley and Ray Palmer made the only acceptable sighting for Tingley Wood near Pirton in 1923.

The sudden decline of Pearl-bordered Fritillary from Hertfordshire closely parallels that of the Small Pearl-bordered Fritillary. Some increases, albeit rather short-lived, can be related to the warmer summers of the 1920s to 1940s, but loss of the more open woodlands and tree-ed commons, as coppicing ceased or overgrowth progressed, caused a gradual decline of this species up to the 1950s. Subsequently poor summer weather over several years and the demise of Rabbits, important herbivores of both woodlands and grasslands, finally quite rapidly eliminated most remaining colonies by the 1960s. The small colony at Bramfield, which persisted until 1978, was found in wide sunny rides with well-developed hardwood fringes to the blocks of conifers, but died out when grasses and shrubs grew up to shade out larval foodplants as woodland ride management was neglected – once again illustrating how vulnerable such species are to environmental changes.

In Britain, Pearl-bordered Fritillary has, usually, a single generation each year, and adults are on the wing in May and June, with first emergences about a fortnight earlier than the first Small Pearl-bordered Fritillaries; there is some overlap between the two species in early June. Pearl-bordered are generally slightly larger, with paler upperwings, than Small Pearl-bordered but are best determined by examination of the hind underwings. These are yellow mottled with orange and bearing black veins; they have seven silver 'pearls' along the outer margin, another near the centre of the wing and a further small one close to the body. Distinct colonies are formed, sometimes with up to a hundred individuals, in sunny open woods where young violets abound, notably Common Dog Violet *Viola riviniana* Rchb. On warm sunny days males may be most active, ranging low to the ground flora searching for the less active females, and taking nectar from spring flowers, particularly Bugle *Ajuga reptans* L. Usually single, but sometimes in groups, eggs may be laid directly on young leaves of violet in sunny situations in clearings and rides, although often these are deposited on other plants or litter close to patches of violets. Together with Glen Castle, the author observed an egg being laid on the margins of unfurling leaves of a low coppiced Field Maple *Acer campestre* L., some thirty centimetres from the nearest violets. In sunny weather the black, yellow-bristled larvae rest openly, frequently on dead leaves, between short feeding forays. In their fourth instar the larvae enter hibernation beneath leaf litter. Feeding is resumed in the following March or April and pupation takes place in dense vegetation, the leaf-like grey-brown chrysalides being most difficult to find.

# Queen of Spain Fritillary

*Argynnis lathonia*   Linnaeus

J. F. Stephens – 1818

This attractive and scarce migrant to Britain has been seen only on three occasions in Hertfordshire since Stephens (1828) wrote 'in plenty, August and September 1818' at Hertford. In 1946 the Hon. R. Gerard saw a Queen of Spain Fritillary near Widford. Two separate observers reported single specimens (probably the same butterfly) in gardens at Radlett in August 1975, and another was seen at Chiswellgreen near St Albans on 29 May 1982. Unconfirmed sightings were made of one at Symonshyde Great Wood in 1976 and of 'possibly two' in a garden at Radlett during 1982.

In flight the Queen of Spain Fritillary, with its black-spotted upperwings, might be mistaken for a Wall or small Silver-washed Fritillary. The hind underwings are most distinctive, with many large silvery or pearly patches which glisten as they catch the light of the sun. This butterfly is well distributed throughout Europe and North Africa and well known for its northern migrations. A few reach the coasts and downs of southern England in most years, generally in late spring, but in favourable years later arrivals are likely. Very occasionally large invasions take place, as in 1945, the best year for records in Britain this century, although apparently none reached Hertfordshire. Very rarely breeding has been noted, with eggs laid on violets to produce a brood in August.

# High Brown Fritillary

*Argynnis adippe*   Denis and Schiffermüller

A. F. Griffith – 1884

Without a good view of the underwings our three large species of fritillary are readily confused. In certain locations all three were to be found on the wing together and some mis-identifications are probably contained within the historical records. Despite these possible errors it is now reasonably certain that, from being formerly quite common

PLATE
page 135

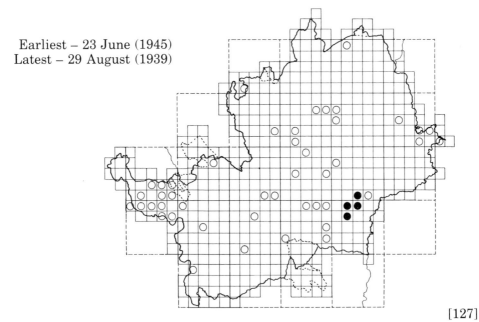

Earliest – 23 June (1945)
Latest – 29 August (1939)

and fairly widespread, High Brown Fritillary is extinct in Hertford-shire. As with so many other species, the local decline of this butterfly closely parallels national trends.

Little note was made of High Brown Fritillary in the literature relating to the 19th century and it is thus difficult to determine the true nature of its status at that time. Perkins (1878), who by his own admission did not know Hertfordshire well, suggested that it might be obtained near St Albans, but regretted that he could give 'no certain information' for he had 'never been in this county when they should be flying'. Griffiths (1884) relates the capture of 'but one specimen' at Symonshyde Great Wood. In 1893 Latchmore and Gatward took specimens at Hitch Wood. In Gibbs (1902) the Hon. L. Walter Roths-child of Tring considered 'that the three larger species of *Argynnis* are much scarcer than formerly' and E. George Elliman, also of Tring, found that High Brown appeared to be much more plentiful than Dark Green 'in the Tring Woods'.

Foster (1916) records seeing and taking 'a fair number' of High Brown Fritillaries at Hitch Wood in 1902. He also refers to its occur-rence in Knebworth Woods and at Tingley Wood near Pirton, stating that it was probably present 'in most of the bigger woods' of north Hertfordshire although 'quite scarce'. Whether or not the High Brown Fritillary was scarce in the last century and spread its range in the county during the first half of this century is a matter of conjecture that may never be determined, although this is suggested by the increased records published by Foster (1937) and from other sources. Populations may well have benefited from the warmer than average summers between the 1920s and 1940s. By the 1940s the full range shown on the distribution map had been attained. It is probable that this had been much the same for many years and that lack of mobility deterred entomologists from investigating certain areas of the county, particularly the north-east. This distribution closely matches those of our other woodland fritillaries, especially Pearl-bordered, and shows that High Brown too, preferred the larger, relatively open coppiced woods and scrubby commons, with adjacent unimproved flowery pastures.

S. B. Hodgson (1939), in his perambulations of west Hertfordshire, found High Brown Fritillary to be 'usually fairly common' at Ashridge between 1929 and 1938, but 'rarely seen' elsewhere in the Tring–Berkhamsted district. He also noted in his diaries small numbers near Champneys, to the west of Berkhamsted, in 1943 and 1944, and on the north side of Hockeridge Wood, south of Berkhamsted, from 1948 to 1951, 'but not since'. A few specimens in St Albans Museum were collected 'near Tring' between 1946 and 1948. By 1950 numbers had noticeably declined at Ashridge: a solitary male seen there in 1955 was the last record for the area. Hodgson (1962) considered that this loss was caused by post-war mowing of woodland paths, plus collecting by 'schoolboys'.

Foster (1946) indicates that High Brown was scarce in the Bishops Stortford region. A few individuals were seen at Albury between 1934 and 1936, at Long Meadow near Bury Green in 1941 and 1944, and at Hoggates Wood near Bishops Stortford in 1944 and 1945. Interest-ingly, the Bishops Stortford Natural History Society (1950) considered this butterfly as 'probably to be found in most of the woods on the Hertfordshire side of our district', a statement not adequately backed up with any records. Most probably, only a few of these woods held small numbers. On 1 August 1951 one High Brown Fritillary was seen in Birchanger Wood in Bishops Stortford and the last authenticated record for the whole of the county was made with a specimen obtained at Long Meadow on 10 July 1978. A possible sighting was made in July 1978 near Standon – an area in which Dark Green and Silver-washed Fritillaries were confirmed in the early 1980s.

High Brown Fritillaries were found at Box Wood near Stevenage and St John's Wood near Walkern in 1943, and described as 'numerous near Walkern' in 1945 by the Rev. W. Greenham. Roger Ferry also found them 'numerous' at Knebworth Woods and took a dozen specimens for his collection. The Letchworth Naturalists' Society regularly visited this area and noted High Brown, together with Silver-washed, to be 'plentiful' on 3 July 1947. 'Many' were also seen there on 9 July 1950, but this was to be the last record for the site, further illustrating the abrupt decline of the species.

Before and during the early 1940s a number of specimens were obtained near Essendon and, 'despite war-time ploughing and felling' at The Roughs and Furze Wood, L. S. Hodson found 'some' on 'headlands left' during 1945. In 1946 this butterfly, was found to be 'common' near Haileybury and seen at St Albans; it was also found at Bricket Wood in the late 1940s, at Welwyn in 1947 and at Symonshyde Great Wood in 1949 and 1950. About 1950 reports were made, probably of singles, from Haileybury, Northaw Great Wood and Broxbourne Woods, and about 1961 from Bramfield Wood and Digswell. The last sightings of this species for the central-southern portions of Hertfordshire were of one at Broxbourne Woods in 1971 and 'one or two' at Balls Wood near Hertford Heath in 1977.

In Hertfordshire there was a general decline of the High Brown Fritillary well before its rapid demise in the 1950s which was to develop into national scarcity. The pattern of this loss is similar to those of the losses of our other woodland fritillaries. Entomologists admit to all too little knowledge of the species' ecology, but it is evident that large areas of sunny, open or coppiced woods with violets and adjacent unimproved grasslands were important factors for its survival. Such habitats were disappearing from the Hertfordshire countryside well before the end of the last century and the rate of loss has certainly accelerated during the course of this. Despite some apparent revivals between about 1920 and the late 1940s, facilitated by warmer summers, populations of High Brown Fritillary were already depleted to dangerously low levels. Poor summers of the late 1950s and 1960s dealt the final blow to the species in Hertfordshire. Although a few remained until the 1970s, it is obvious that habitats were not suitable to support viable colonies: on top of the climatic changes were many other factors affecting the environment, including the loss of larval foodplants, shaded out by the continued overgrowth of woods, due to the cessation of management and reduction in grazing by Rabbits, reafforestation with conifers, and the isolation, fragmentation and clearance of suitable sites through agricultural and other developments.

Plate 15 (*Top*)  Red Admiral (*Vanessa atalanta* [p. 102]
(*Bottom*)  Painted Lady (*Cynthia cardui*) [p. 103]

130

Plate 16 (*Top*)   Small Tortoiseshell (*Aglais urticae*) [p. 108]
        (*Bottom*)   Camberwell Beauty (*Nymphalis antiopa*) [p. 114]

131

High Brown Fritillaries appear from late June, with the main flight period during July. In some years a few may persist into August – an exceptionally late sighting was made in 1939 when S. B. Hodgson located one at Ashridge on 29 August. There may be an overlap with both Dark Green and Silver-washed Fritillaries and it is possible that all these species may be found together. Confusion is, however, most likely between High Brown and Dark Green, which are smaller than the Silver-washed. Both High Brown and Dark Green have golden brown, black-spotted upperwings and are best determined by examination of the hind underwings. High Brown has two bands of silver spots towards the outer margins, within which is a row of silver-centred red spots, not found in the generally greener-underwinged Dark Green.

Colonies of High Brown Fritillary are mainly self-contained and cover relatively large areas, often several hectares in extent, with breeding only occurring in sheltered, sunny, open parts of woods where violets are abundant. This rather specialised habitat requirement is probably the major factor relating to declines. Their flight is rapid, often with soaring visits into the treetops where they roost at night or in poor weather. When feeding they are particularly attracted to sunlit brambles and thistles, sometimes gathering at favoured patches in numbers. At Pitstone Common, just over the county boundary in Buckinghamshire, S. B. Hodgson saw eleven feeding on the only known patch of Devils-bit Scabious *Succisa pratensis* Moench on 25 July 1951 and seven on thistles in a nearby dry pond on 23 July 1952. At times some individuals may wander some distance from the main colony. Eggs are laid singly on dead litter or deep within bushes and coppice stools close to patches of Common Dog Violet *Viola riviniana* Rchb. It is probable that other *Viola* species may be utilised. After overwintering the eggs hatch in the spring and the spiny brown larvae crawl to the violet plants where they feed by day on young leaves. Difficult to find, the dark brown, gold-pointed pupae are formed, suspended from twigs, deep within vegetation.

# Dark Green Fritillary

*Argynnis aglaja*   Linnaeus

Haileybury Natural Science Society – *c* 1873

The distribution map suggests that, apart from the central region of Hertfordshire, there has been little apparent change in the frequency of Dark Green Fritillary. This is misleading, for there have been significant reductions especially in the last thirty years or so. Most of the more recent sightings relate to small numbers and are from a few remaining sites that support chalk grassland and scrub or woods with extensive grassy rides or open scrub. Dark Green, unlike the other

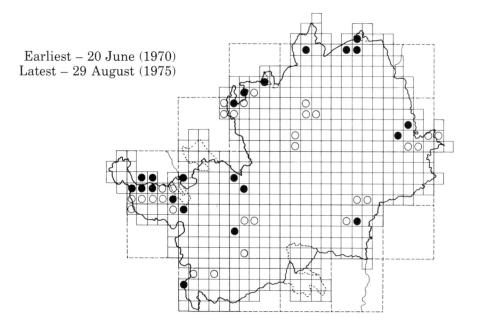

Earliest – 20 June (1970)
Latest – 29 August (1975)

woodland fritillaries, although dependent on violets and recorded in woods, has never been typical of coppice-managed sites.

In common with the other fritillaries, very few records of Dark Green were made in the 19th century and the first report from the county was from the Haileybury area in 1873. Whether this suggests that it, too, was scarce and increased in the 1920s to 1940s is open to conjecture. Apart from Haileybury, where Dark Green was again recorded about 1888, Gibbs (1902) notes that Elliman considered the High Brown to be 'much more plentiful' than the Dark Green 'in the Tring Woods', and lists three further sites, Grove Wood and Browns Lane, both near Tring, and Long Meadow near Bury Green, where Charles Mellow saw specimens in 1895 and 1896.

Foster (1916) makes no mention of this butterfly – his Hertfordshire specimens, from the neighbourhood of Hitchin, were not obtained until the 1940s – but he records (1934), 'Pearl-bordered, Silver-washed, Dark Green and High Brown' as 'occurring sparingly only' in the Hitchin region. Further sites, covering much of this species' known county distribution, are listed by Foster (1937), including Therfield Heath, Highdown near Pirton, Knebworth Woods, Ashridge, Berkhamsted, Chorleywood and Broxbourne Woods, but no indication is given of abundances. This butterfly is strong-winged and prone to wander, but how far is uncertain, as research in recent years suggests that it may not be as mobile as was formerly thought, possibly only ranging from breeding sites to feed.

A little information regarding the status of Dark Green comes from other references. From 1922 to 1930 this butterfly was known from a relatively small area of chalk grassland and scrub (Ledgeside Plantation) at Chesfield near Graveley; Ray Palmer found it 'abundant' there on 20 July 1923 and discovered a larva on violet leaves on 5 June 1930. From 1929 to 1938 S. B. Hodgson (1939) noted 'this species is rarely seen in the Tring–Berkhamsted district elsewhere than Ashridge', where it was 'widely distributed but scarce'. His diaries relate that from 1935 to the 1940s 'both sexes used to fly with "High

Plate 17 (*Top*)   Comma (*Polygonia c-album*) [p. 118]
(*Bottom*)   Peacock (*Inachis io*) [p. 116]

134

Plate 18 (*Top*)  Pearl-bordered Fritillary (*Boloria euphrosyne*) [p. 123]
(*Bottom*)  High Brown Fritillary (*Argynnis adippe*) [p. 127]

135

Brown" round Sallow Copse, Ashridge'. He also records 'both sexes quite common at Dancers End (Buckinghamshire) in July 1935' and that numbers diminished there up to 1951, when the habitat was finally 'overgrown with thorn and briar'.

From the 1940s to the 1970s a few changes in the Hertfordshire status of Dark Green Fritillary were noticed. In 1943 it was found at Stocking Plantations near Bury Green, and was 'frequent' in the nearby Long Meadow, but by 1945 it was regarded as scarce in the area studied by the Bishops Stortford Natural History Society, the only other reports being of one seen in Birchanger Wood, Bishops Stortford in 1952 and another at Long Meadow on 11 July 1956. On the Chalk hills overlapping the county border with Bedfordshire, about Hexton and Pegsdon, various recorders found the butterfly to be common from 1943 to at least 1948. There were sightings of small numbers, mostly individuals, in the late 1940s at St Albans, Knebworth, Whippendell and Bricket Woods. The downs of the west, notably just outside the county, at the Ivinghoe and Pitstone Hills, used to support fair-sized breeding colonies, which were no doubt responsible for many of those seen across the border in Hertfordshire. Never the less a number of sites, such as Berkhamsted Common and Aldbury Nowers, held viable colonies before they became overgrown following the demise of Rabbits, and suffered the effects of the poor summers of the 1950s and 1960s. In this region ploughing, too, caused the loss of much of the Dark Green's breeding habitat, especially the important site at Incombe Hole in the early 1960s, and this exacerbated the effects of the other habitat changes. Significant reductions in the numbers of observations followed, although small resident populations still occur which, in good years may be reasonably numerous.

From 1970 to 1983 only a small number of records were made, mostly as singles in the Tring–Aldbury area. Away from here the other reports came from Tingley Wood near Pirton, on 20 June 1970 (when one 'in perfect condition' was found, perhaps suggesting local breeding), Harpenden on 1 August 1972, Therfield Heath near Royston (also suggestive of local breeding) from 1973 to 1977, Hoddesdon Park Wood about 1975, Ickleford (where a very late specimen, in the Woodhall Collection at North Hertfordshire Museums, was taken) on 29 August 1975, Potterscrouch plantations in 1976, Ravensdell Wood near Studham in 1982, Harpenden Common in July 1982, near Pegsdon in 1982, and near Albury in 1982 and on 6 August 1983 (which again suggests a small colony).

During the Survey years 1984 to 1986 very few records were made and there was no positive evidence of breeding. In these years the small numbers observed at Aldbury Nowers and Berkhamsted Common may relate to possible breeding for, in some places, there are small habitats that appear to be still congenial. It should, however, be noted that numbers were found to be particularly good on the nearby Ivinghoe hills, especially in 1986, and the possibility of 'wanderers' cannot be ruled out. Singles were seen at the Hexton Chalk Pit Nature Reserve on 7 July 1984 and at Greys, near Therfield Heath, in August of the same year. A melanic variant was found in 1984 on the county border with Buckinghamshire near Chorleywood. In 1985 and 1986 up to two were seen again at Ravensdell Wood near

Studham, and on 19 July 1986 there was a single at the Ashwell Quarries Nature Reserve.

Formerly less widespread, and certainly less numerous, than many of the other fritillaries, the Dark Green is now, though very scarce, one of Hertfordshire's only two remaining resident fritillaries. Fluctuations in numbers still occur, probably related to variation in summer weather, but the apparent trend is downwards, as loss of habitat continues. Small scale, very localised breeding probably still sporadically occurs but the long term outlook for this species in the county is bleak.

Active from late June to mid-August, Dark Green Fritillaries may be found in small numbers along rides or within open woods; however, they are generally more typical of exposed, lightly grazed, rough grasslands and open scrub of Chalk downs and commons, where they are more numerous. They form relatively self-contained colonies, which in other parts of Britain may contain large numbers, but as in Hertfordshire are frequently small, with only the odd individual being seen. Their rapid flight can make differentiation from the other large fritillaries, Comma and Wall, difficult and they are best determined at rest, particularly when feeding on thistles or other flowers. Examination of the hind underwings is important: the Dark Green has numerous silver patches on a, usually, greener ground than High Brown but lacks the silver-centred red spots of the latter. Silver spots along the margins of the under forewings are also diagnostic of Dark Green.

Dark Green Fritillaries often select relatively small breeding grounds within small parts of their favoured range. Eggs are laid singly amongst litter or vegetation near to sunlit clumps of Hairy Violet *Viola hirta* L., Common Dog Violet *V. riviniana* Rchb. or Early Dog Violet *V. reichenbachiana* Bor. Emergent larvae consume their eggshells and enter hibernation. Feeding begins in the following spring and appears to be restricted to periods of sunshine, when the mobile purplish, spiny larvae inflict characteristic damage to the margins of violet leaves. Pupation takes place deep within grassy tussocks or dense vegetation.

# Silver-washed Fritillary

*Argynnis paphia*   Linnaeus

Rev. C. M. Perkins – 1878

The largest and most striking of our fritillaries, the Silver-washed, was first noted in Hertfordshire by Perkins (1878) as 'common in woods near St Albans'. Other early records imply that it was found in many of the larger woods of the county. It noticeably declined around the turn of the century, but increased again in the warmer summers of the 1920s and 1940s, only to suffer many local extinctions in the

PLATE page 154

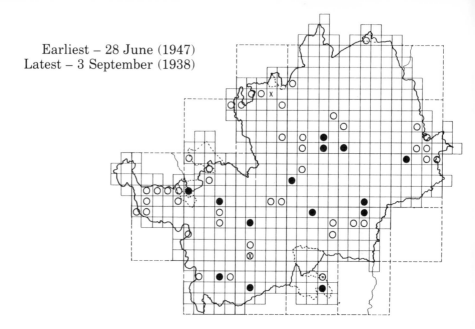

Earliest – 28 June (1947)
Latest – 3 September (1938)

following two decades. In other parts of southern and western Britain, the indications are that Silver-washed Fritillary is still contracting its range, although in places it is still reasonably numerous and widespread.

Gibbs (1902) notes the comments of the Hon. L. Walter Rothschild that 'the three larger species of *Argynnis* are much scarcer than formerly' and only lists records from Stevenage (= Knebworth Woods, where Silver-washed Fritillary was 'sometimes very common'), Hitchin (= Highdown near Pirton), Bricket Wood, East Barnet, Watford, Longcroft and Brown's Lane, Tring, and at Sandridge (presumably Symonshyde Great Wood). Another was at Symonshyde Great Wood on 1 August 1904 (Gibbs, 1905); in recording this sighting Gibbs emphasises the scarcity of the Silver-washed Fritillary in the county around that time.

Foster (1916) relates seeing or taking specimens of Silver-washed Fritillary in Hitch Wood, Knebworth Woods and 'one or two' of the other larger woods of the Hitchin district, 'always as single individuals, usually on thistles', but regarded it as 'generally very scarce'. On 26 July 1919, S. R. Bowden obtained several specimens at Tingley Field Plantation, which is just in Bedfordshire, a short distance west of Tingley Wood near Pirton. In 1922 one was seen at Wilbury Hill near Letchworth and in 1930 a female was taken at Bourne Gutter, north of Bovingdon. S. B. Hodgson (1939) thought that the Silver-washed was 'in danger of disappearing', for it was rarely seen in the Tring–Berkhamsted district, other than at Ashridge, and even there it was 'extremely local and scarce'. He found several males and one female in clearings at Sallow Copse, Ashridge on 15 August 1934. In the same year in the east of the county, a single Silver-washed Fritillary was noted at Patmore Hall Wood near Albury; and the only other pre-1940 records summarised by Foster (1937) were from Apsley End, Chorleywood, Broxbourne Woods and Beech Wood, Barnet.

From the early 1940s to the mid-1950s Silver-washed Fritillary appeared to increase quite significantly in some of the larger semi-natural wooded areas of Hertfordshire, and thereafter again declined. Isolated records from Roger Ferry's garden at Fulling Mill, Welwyn and Lilley Hoo, west of Hitchin, in the early 1940s suggested range expansion. Foster (1946) notes its spread in the Bishops Stortford district and 'quite a number were seen' at Long Meadow and the woods adjacent to Bury Green in 1941, Thorley Wood in 1943 and Hoggates Wood in 1944 and 1945. Observations were made in 1955 at Stocking Wood Plantation and Bloodhounds Wood, a specimen taken at Long Meadow on 15 July 1956, and a single sighting at Much Hadham in the very hot summer of 1976, were the last for that district.

Silver-washed was present at Whippendell Woods near Watford from 1942 to 1949, and from 1956 until 1959 it was regarded as 'fairly plentiful' there. A subsequent decline is noted by Penrose (1983) – indeed 'it seemed to have disappeared' by 1980 – but a single seen in 1982 may perhaps suggest a small relict population, although as with all the larger fritillaries, this species may wander. The possibilities of introductions or the escape of captive-bred specimens can not be discounted.

In Knebworth Woods the species was common in 1942 and on 9 July 1945 they were flying in company with High Browns. On 7 July 1946 Roger Ferry found Silver-washed to be 'just hatching' and took ten specimens, including the form *valezina*. The last record for Knebworth Woods was made on 28 June 1947, maybe showing that the colony was over-collected by Ferry. A number of specimens were taken at Bricket Wood in 1948 and at Symonshyde Great Wood between 1949 and 1956. At Sallow Copse, Ashridge, three males were seen on 4 August 1950 and in the same year individuals were recorded from Aldbury Nowers, Highdown near Pirton, Northaw Great Wood, Broxbourne Woods and, as 'rarer visitors' to Goldings Wood near Haileybury, prompting Bell (1953) to suggest that Silver-washed Fritillary was 'gaining a firmer hold'. There were only three further records for the south-western part of the county between 1950 and 1970, 'several in clearings' at High Scrubs, south of Tring, on 16 July 1952, 'a courting pair in a fir wood' below Berkhamsted Common on 10 August 1953, and a sighting at Bricket Wood in 1960.

Silver-washed Fritillary obviously declined in Hertfordshire from the late 1950s to the 1970s and, for a period, may well have become extinct, as a result of overgrowth of coppices and woodland rides, with the shading of violets, and a series of cooler than average summers. There are some indications that, perhaps benefiting from the hot summers of 1976 and 1977, this butterfly is returning to the county, although numbers are still very low. Individuals were seen at Hudnall Common and Oughtonhead Common near Hitchin in 1981, and in 1982 at Balls Wood near Hertford Heath and Whippendell Woods. A fine male was photographed feeding on *Buddleia* sp. in a garden at Aston near Stevenage in August 1983. During the Survey years several were recorded in 1984, with three along a bridleway east of Hatfield Park in July, two at Prae Wood near St Albans on 22 July and singles along the Ayot Way near Ayot Green, Hoddesdon Park Wood on 8 July and 'on dried pond mud' at Astonbury Wood near Stevenage in mid-August. One found in a garden at Bushey on 26

July 1985 is suggestive of an escape from captive breeding. On 1 August 1986 two were seen along a sunny ride at Balls Wood, on 5th another was observed 'basking on bramble' at Stags End, north of Hemel Hempstead, and on 5th too, a probable was sighted which 'apparently hatched from a violet clump and flew away', in a large garden at Richmond Road, New Barnet, which is fairly close to some former known sites.

Silver-washed Fritillary can be readily obtained from entomological dealers and easily reared in captivity: hence the possibilities of escapes are quite high. In early June 1986 four males and four females were released at Bricket Wood in an attempt to re-establish the species in an area where it had been extinct for at least twenty years. Fortunately this was reported and any future sightings at the site will take due account of the release. It cannot be stressed enough that such 'introductions' can have far-reaching conservation implications for many species and their habitats; anyone contemplating a similar release as a conservation measure is very seriously advised to follow closely the principles and guidelines laid down for such introductions by the Joint Committee for the Conservation of British Insects.

The latest of our fritillaries to emerge, Silver-washed, is on the wing from mid-July to mid-August. Larger than the other species, males in particular are fairly easily identified by their heavily black-spotted and -lined deep orange upperwings. Females have browner upperwings, with larger black spots, but no streaks, appearing very dark both in flight and at rest. Both sexes have distinctive green hind underwings, cross-marked with four silvery streaks. A female form *valezina*, much sought by collectors, is occasionally found in Hertfordshire; this has a pink suffusion on the under forewings and a dark green ground colour to the upperwings.

As with all the fritillaries of woodlands, Silver-washed form discrete colonies covering quite large areas in relatively open woods with violets, from which they may range into adjacent fields, lanes and hedgerows to feed on thistles and brambles. They appear to be rather more tolerant of shade, which may account for the fact that they have survived slightly better than the other woodland fritillaries. These two factors give some clues to the overall declines of the fritillaries. First, blocks of open, semi-natural woodland, large enough to maintain viable populations, have disappeared from the Hertfordshire landscape, and those that remain are mostly too dense or shaded for breeding and increasingly fragmented and isolated. Periods of poor summers lead to local extinctions because the already low populations are unable to cope with extreme conditions.

Females search out clumps of violets, usually Common Dog Violet *Viola riviniana* Rchb., beneath a thin tree canopy where reasonably high levels of sunlight penetrate. Eggs are then deposited within crevices in the bark of nearby trees, a few feet from the ground. About a fortnight later larvae hatch and immediately enter hibernation on the tree trunk. In the following spring larvae descend to feed by day on the young shoots and leaves of violets. Full grown larvae are most striking, with two yellow stripes running along the back of the soft brown body, which is well endowed with spines. They cause characteristic damage to the lobes of violet leaves and may wander considerable distances to feed and bask in the sun. The beautiful gold-tipped brown pupae are difficult to find amongst dense vegetation.

# Marsh Fritillary

*Eurodryas aurinia*   Rottemburg

Haileybury Natural Science Society – 1873

This attractive butterfly, sometimes, formerly, called the Greasy Frit- PLATE
illary, was always rather local in Hertfordshire and became extinct page 154
before 1960. Although its former range in the county appears to
coincide closely with those of the woodland fritillaries, Marsh Fritillary was always found in flowery open grassland sites, where foodplant
of its larvae, Devils-bit Scabious *Succisa pratensis* Moench was abun-

Earliest – 12 May (1945)
  Latest – 13 June (1942)

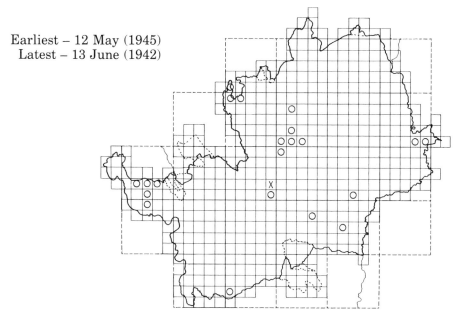

dant. These sites included lightly grazed damp unimproved meadows,
boggy heaths, wide woodland rides and large glades, wood pastures
and certain parts of the dry chalk downs. Some of these sites were
integral with woodland complexes. The extirpation of Marsh Fritillary
in Hertfordshire is directly related to the loss of these habitats, with
final elimination resulting from the effects of poor summers in the
1950s, a pattern which has been noted throughout much of eastern
and southern England.

It is intriguing that very few observations were made of Marsh
Fritillary until the 1940s. The Haileybury Natural Science Society
found it in their area about 1873, and again from 1889 to 1901.

Durrant (1885 and 1888) relates an observation of these butterflies, at Burleigh Heath near Knebworth Woods in 1881, by William Hill of Hitchin. It should be noted that A. F. Griffith, in an appendix to Durrant (1885), confused this record, wrongly stating it as a sighting from Knebworth Woods, not Burleigh Heath, by a Mr Christian, an error which both Gibbs (1902) and Foster (1937) repeated. Gibbs (1902) dismisses specimens collected by the Rev. H. Harpur Crewe at Drayton Beauchamp and published as Hertfordshire records by Newman (1874), on the evidence of Elliman, who considered that they were obtained just over the county boundary in Buckinghamshire.

Foster (1916 and 1934) was unable to find Marsh Fritillary in the Knebworth area and concluded that it had 'disappeared from this district'. This was probably an over-statement, for it is likely that the species did remain in small numbers. Only four further records, however, without any indications of abundance, were made before the 1940s, at Aldbury Nowers and on the banks of the canal near Tring Station in 1922, at Oxhey Wood in 1938, and 'in a field by Fishers Green' near Stevenage in the late 1930s.

No doubt resulting from the warmer summers there was a significant increase in records throughout the 1940s. Populations are known to build up rapidly and develop dispersal tendencies during periods of warmer sunny weather and may thus become rather more obvious. In many of the sites where they were thought to be extinct it is most likely that small numbers remained, but were not very active and therefore missed by entomologists. From 1941 to 1951 specimens were taken and seen at a site on the steep canal banks to the east of Tring, possibly the same site where the species was seen in 1922. Up to thirty females were seen on one day, suggesting quite a healthy colony. After 1952 there were no other sightings there, although, as S. B. Hodgson noted in his diaries, it had 'spread and was found on the railway bank' near Parkhill Farm and had 'reached Aldbury Nowers', where on 12 May 1945 there were 'many' along the top of the slope. Until 1956 it remained at Aldbury Nowers in 'good numbers but became scarcer from 1957' and was extinct there by 1965. Hodgson thought that 'parasitic ichneumons' had possibly attacked the larvae and reduced its 'numbers below the necessary survival density', and also notes that 'certain London collectors may have contributed to its total disappearance'. Both these pressures could have had deleterious effects, particularly in a situation where numbers were already dwindling as suitable habitat was being lost through overgrowth and poor weather was affecting the survival rates of adults and larvae.

In 1942 a specimen of Marsh Fritillary was taken at Long Meadow near Bury Green. Between 1942 and 1945 a few were seen on the Chalk hills at Hexton and Lilley Hoo where, because of their apparent sudden appearance, it was suggested by some entomologists that introductions might have been made. No evidence to support these claims can be found and again small relict colonies probably remained undetected for many years. From 1943 to 1945 Foster found several at Norton Green and, 'in damp clearings' at Knebworth Woods. In 1944, a small colony was located by Sidney Bowden on the railway bank between Knebworth and Stevenage. Bowden, in the *Journal of the Letchworth Naturalists' Society* (1947 to 1953), describes a 'restricted

North Herts locality' known to him from 1946, which had 'eight or nine nests of larvae' in 1947, and a few adults in 1948, but 'was extensively burnt in 1949' so that the colony was exterminated. The exact location of this site is not revealed in the literature although it is possibly indicated by Bowden (1953) when he writes that Knebworth Wood 'was searched again – it was probably too early for the Marsh Fritillary, even if it persists there'.

From 1943 a colony was known at Tom's Wood Pasture near Bishops Stortford; when the site was threatened with war-time ploughing in 1944 the colony was 'transferred to a near by site', where a few remained until 1946, 'but not after'. Another small colony of Marsh Fritillary found at Camfield Place, Essendon in 1944, was destroyed by 'agricultural development' about 1950. In 1946 there were sightings at Wormley Wood and in two locations near Codicote, Crouch Green and The Node; at the latter site it was seen again in 1947. In 1948 and 1949 rather vague reference was made to a colony at a site 'a few miles from Hitchin', possibly on the Chalk hills near Hexton, which 'was grazed in 1950, to the detriment of the species'. A specimen was taken at Symonshyde Great Wood in 1949 and a few larvae were found at Wiggington near Tring in 1950.

The increases enjoyed by Marsh Fritillary during the 1940s were short-lived and all colonies, except those on certain sheltered slopes of the Chalk in the south-west of the county, were extinct by the mid-1950s from overgrowth, ploughing, drainage or improvement of grasslands. Poor summers, scrub encroachment and, possibly, collecting exterminated the remainder before 1960. A factor which has been noted in other parts of Britain and may have been responsible for some of the Hertfordshire losses, paradoxically, is the generation by isolated colonies of *too many* larvae. If there are too many larvae, they may consume all the available Devils-bit Scabious before they are ready for pupation, and in extreme cases none may survive to pupate. An unsuccessful attempt was made to establish a colony near Wheathampstead in 1983; although some adults were seen in the following year there were none in 1985.

Marsh Fritillaries breed in self-contained colonies, on sometimes quite small areas of flowery grassland and numbers are significantly reduced by cool weather. They have been found to be really successful only where rather lush stands of Devils-bit Scabious abound in sunny sheltered situations. This, as noted above, may be in two quite different habitat types, on lightly grazed or cut dry chalk grassland or rather damp, sometimes acid, unimproved meadows or heath. Some colonies may occur in recently cleared woods or along rides, but they are ousted if trees and shrubs shade their larval foodplants. Adults can be rather variable in size and colouration and are on the wing from late May to mid-June, a short flight period which can be seriously interrupted by even short spells of poor weather and late frosts. Their upperwings are reddish-orange, less golden than the other fritillaries, with yellow or sometimes white, patches, distinctive black veins and blurry cross bars. Towards the margin of the upper and lower hind-wings is a series of characteristic black dots. Beneath, the wings appear dull reddish with a pale yellowish, central band and several spots, and fine black markings. Some adults have a dull waxy or 'greasy' sheen to their wings, from which the species derived its earlier name of Greasy Fritillary.

Mated females prefer to lay their large batches of eggs, often piled up, beneath longer leaves of Devils-bit Scabious. On hatching the spiny black larvae spin a matted communal web beneath which they bask between periods of feeding. Research has shown that, beneath this web, the larvae maintain a relatively steady temperature of 30°C, even on cool days. When they are about half-grown they produce a denser web, within which hibernation takes place. Feeding resumes in the following spring and, as they grow and move from plant to plant, the larvae become less gregarious. As noted above, such large concentrations of larvae in a small area can result in mass starvation unless outside influences reduce numbers; parasitism from *Apanteles* wasps, for example, can bring levels down to supportable proportions. Over-parasitism or predation, however, could obviously be detrimental to the survival of isolated colonies and may well have been an important factor at some of the former Hertfordshire sites. Pupation takes place in dense vegetation, where the cream coloured black-spotted chrysalides are difficult to find.

# Speckled Wood

*Pararge aegeria*   Linnaeus

Thomas Dandridge – *c* 1700

PLATE
page 155

Speckled Wood has for a long time been accorded special regard amongst Hertfordshire entomologists; it is a butterfly with a chequered history in Britain and, even before the Hertfordshire Natural History Society elected to undertake a long-term study of its status from about 1916, it was already in the annals of entomological history of the county. Two specimens illustrated by James Petiver (1702–1709 and 1717) and named 'The Enfield Eye' and 'The Brown Enfield Eye' have been easily identified by later entomologists as being Speckled Woods, probably female and male respectively. Petiver notes that the 'Enfield Eye' was found at Enfield Chase – indeed, there were 'several of them on that Chace and elsewhere, but not common'; 'The Brown Enfield Eye' was observed by Thomas Dandridge at Watford 'towards the end of July' and this sighting constitutes the first ever butterfly record (so far known) for Hertfordshire. There are no other reports of Speckled Wood until the latter half of the 19th century.

A. E. Gibbs made a detailed study of the 'satyrid' or 'brown' butterflies with special reference to their status in Hertfordshire. Much of the lengthy paper (1916) delivered in his Presidential address to the Anniversary meeting of the Hertfordshire Natural History Society on 31 March 1916 was devoted to the Speckled Wood which, at that time, he thought to be extinct in the county. Gibbs stated that few data were available and urged members of the Society to find out more.

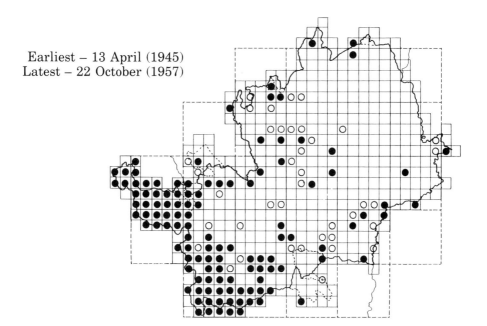

Earliest – 13 April (1945)
Latest – 22 October (1957)

The next record to come after Petiver's publication was of a sighting near Haileybury about 1880. National data show that Speckled Wood suffered a significant retraction of range from the late 19th to the early 20th century, and was probably, at least, very scarce in Hertford-shire at some earlier date. Gibbs concluded that Speckled Wood had never been 'really abundant anywhere in Hertfordshire' and 'in recent years had been gradually declining in numbers'. The only other 19th century records were from Sandridge (probably Symonshyde Great Wood), Oxhey Wood near Watford, and Stubbings Wood near Tring in the late 1880s, and between Knebworth Station and Knebworth Park in 1893.

Specimens in Dr Grellet's Collection at North Hertfordshire Museums were taken at Wain Wood near Preston about 1900 to 1902. In 1901 or 1902 H. T. Matthews of Stevenage informed Gibbs that Speckled Wood was 'fairly common' near woods in his neighbourhood, and other observers reported that it was 'in more than one spot in the vicinity of Tring'. A single specimen was captured just inside the county border near Chorleywood in 1915. It would appear that, although severely reduced in its numbers, the Speckled Wood did not become extinct in Hertfordshire as Gibbs has thought but, as Hodgson (1938) points out, remained in small numbers, especially in the exten-sive woodlands south of Tring. It is of course possible that there might have been a county extinction during the earlier part of the 19th century and that these records relate to the kinds of fluctuations that were to be more closely documented later this century.

During the 1920s sporadic reports were made at Northaw Great Wood, Broxbourne Woods, Haileybury and in the woods south of Tring, mainly in Buckinghamshire, where, in 1921, Speckled Woods were 'well represented'. It is fairly clear, as noted above, that a national decline was detected which has not been adequately explained, but which was highlighted by the subsequent expansion of this species. Possible factors put forward to explain the decline are fall in annual mean temperatures in the last quarter of the 19th century, the expansion of Rabbits throughout the last century, perhaps, overgrazing woodland habitats, and lengthened coppice cycles, which failed to provide the right conditions for breeding.

Hodgson (1936) records that Speckled Wood was found in the hot dry summer of 1933, 'in several habitats where it was not usually seen in south-west Hertfordshire', and that it was well established in small numbers at Tring, Ashridge, Berkhamsted and near Watford. Further sightings were made in 1935 and 1936 at Flaunden, and at Broxbourne Woods in 1936. These signalled a gradual spread of the species, which was no doubt mainly promoted by the series of warmer summers, the development of shadier uncoppiced woodlands and, perhaps, some controls over Rabbits.

From 1939 to 1946 Speckled Woods were noted at Letchworth. In 1940 they were rare at Chipperfield, but they were common by 1945, and had reached the woods at Symonshyde, Hertford Heath and near Studham in 1944. The species became common in the Tring–Ashridge area by 1943 and in 1945 had spread eastwards to be found in small numbers near Walkern and Bishops Stortford. Before 1950 most of the full range shown on the distribution map had been occupied, although the stronghold always remained in the drier woods of the south-west, much of the eastern and central parts of the county, with extensive arable lands on the Boulder Clay and decalcified Boulder Clay, and dense urban and industrial areas on the River Terrace Gravels, being generally unsuitable to the spread and colonisation by Speckled Woods.

From 1951 to 1969 Speckled Wood noticeably declined once again, probably as a result of the succession of poor summers. It disappeared from many former haunts and the only reports throughout the 1950s were from Symonshyde Great Wood from 1951 to 1959, at Willian near Letchworth in 1952, Oughtonhead near Hitchin in 1953, and near Bishops Stortford in 1959. No records were received by the County Recorder from the south-west until 1964, when it was stated to be widespread but 'apparently declining', and in 1969 none could be found in the Tring area. In 1967, one was seen at Well Wood, Northaw. Numbers picked up slightly in 1970 with reports from Tring and Frithsden Beeches near Berkhamsted. In the following two years indications of another, and continuing, expansion were detected, with 'several in the Tring–Berkhamsted area, one at Broxbourne Wood and about twenty at Bricket Wood'. No doubt facilitated by the series of better summers, warmer autumns and shadier woods and rides, numbers increased and expanded quite rapidly. Speckled Woods were seen at Therfield Heath in 1974, in the Hitchin area from 1975, at Knebworth Woods in 1976, and from 1981 near Bishops Stortford. Following the drought of 1976 numbers fell sharply, but a fairly rapid recovery was aided by the species' ability to produce more than one generation a year. Expansion has been mainly from the south and west, but there is evidence of the occupation of the Bishops Stortford area from the east, as populations in Hatfield Forest, Essex, increased and spread. Results from the Survey years, 1984 to 1986, suggest that Speckled Wood, like the White Admiral, is continuing to expand, and has nearly re-occupied all of its former documented range within the county. A number of records relate to sightings in the autumn, often of singles, which may be a prelude to colonisation if weather conditions remain suitable, a situation which closely resembles the return of the Comma to Hertfordshire half a century ago.

As with the White Admiral, Speckled Wood is able to live and breed in quite shady woodlands. The recent spread shows its abilities for colonisation of certain dense woods, abandoned coppices, overgrown commons and even young conifer plantations, although apparently suitable but isolated sites, without connecting leafy lanes or hedge-rows, seem to remain inaccessible. Overwintering can be in either the larval or pupal stage, which produces a complex succession of generations in the following year and, in turn, usually three main flight periods, from April to May, May and June and August to October. Adults on the wing from August into October can be from either of the earlier generations and may themselves, in good years, produce a further generation before the onset of winter.

Speckled Woods are easily identified as they bask, wings open, along rides or in beams of sunlight amongst the trees. Dark brown upper-wings are boldly speckled with creamy yellow spots and four white-pupilled, creamy-margined, black spots, one near the tip of the upper forewing and three close to the margin of the upper hindwing. Males are slightly smaller and less boldly marked than females and in the summer brood both sexes are slightly paler. Beneath, the blurry patterning of light brown and grey resembles a dead leaf. There are small subtle 'mould spots' on the margin of the hind underwing and a single conspicuous eyespot near the apex of the fore underwing. In flight the dappled wings blend superbly with shafted woodland sunlight.

Feeding is mainly on honeydew in the treetops, but frequently numbers of Speckled Woods gather with other butterflies to feed on bramble flowers in sunny rides or hedgerows. Usually only ones or twos are seen, particularly males who set up territories in glades or rides waiting for passing females. Spiralling chases with other males are frequent; those that hold territories seldom lose out in such encounters and return to preferred sunlit perches to bask. Eggs are laid singly on the blades of shaded grasses, mostly Cocksfoot *Dactylis glomerata* L. and Common Couch *Agropyron repens* L. The day-feeding green, faintly white-and-yellow-lined, larvae are surprisingly difficult to find, as are the green to brown pupae formed amongst dense vegetation.

# Wall

*Lasiommata megera* Linnaeus

Haileybury Natural Science Society – 1878

PLATE
page 155

Little indication is given of the status of this attractive butterfly in Hertfordshire during the 19th century. Perkins (1878), who was not really familiar with the county and admitted to being not available to study butterflies here from June to mid-August, described the Wall as 'universally common – and you may see it in advanced spring, and again in autumn, sunning itself upon a scorching wall, or flying deftly

Earliest – 17 April (1949)
Latest – 19 October (1947)

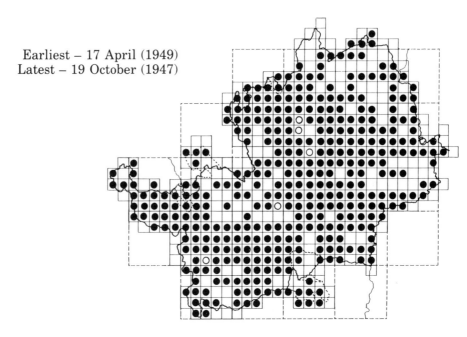

along any warm bank skirting a dusty road', which may have been quite apt for the mid-19th century. Heath, Pollard and Thomas (1984) point out that there is a northern climatic limit to the range of the Wall in Britain and that poor summers of the late 19th and early part of this century caused population reductions and retractions of this range. Gibbs (1902) only lists a handful of records from Stevenage, Hitchin, Knebworth, Sandridge, St Albans, Tring, Watford, Oxhey, Haileybury, East Barnet, and Cheshunt. In his paper on the Satyrid butterflies (1916) he further states that this species was 'now very scarce' in the south and west of Hertfordshire, having 'disappeared from many of its old localities', the last sightings in the St Albans area being in June 1902. In the northern part of the county, according to Foster (1916), it was still 'comparatively common' although 'it might be considered peculiarly local' with 'no apparent diminution in its numbers'.

During the first two decades of this century the Wall was sufficiently

148

scarce in south Hertfordshire for any sightings to excite entomologists. C. H. Jackson (1921) records netting a battered specimen near St Albans in the spring of 1914, and obtaining 'quite a number of specimens' from the second brood in the same year. In 1915 the spring brood was again low in numbers but in August the species was 'distinctly plentiful' around St Albans. Numbers increased and spread so much in 1916 that Jackson reckoned the Wall to be 'the most ubiquitous and common butterfly of its season'. With southern Britain being at the north-western edge of the Wall's European range, even quite subtle climatic variations can affect its numbers. Several subsequent reports of marked population changes can be related to 'good and poor' summers. Hodgson (1936) particularly noted a significant increase, in the fine summer of 1933, around Berkhamsted, despite the fact that the spring brood had not been observed and that, 'for many years it had been generally very scarce and regarded as a vanishing species in the counties round London, but now and then a hot dry summer comes along and there is a temporary revival'.

Throughout the 1940s, related to the series of fine summers, there was an easterly expansion of the Wall in Britain and the species became 'widespread and plentiful' in Hertfordshire, although the loss of some of the Chalk downs and former unimproved pastures to wartime ploughing presumably limited its abundance. In the fine, long summer of 1945 a partial third brood was recorded in October. Poor weather in the 1950s and 1960s, coupled with environmental factors – intensification of agriculture, improvement of grasslands, and the scrub encroachment of downs and commons following the demise of Rabbits – caused a marked decrease in the abundance of the Wall and it went from a number of its former locations. A revival, which started in the early 1970s, was temporarily halted by the drought of 1976, when foodplants of the summer larvae were desiccated. Numbers built up again slowly to a peak in 1983, fell dramatically in 1985, and were quite reasonable in 1986, illustrating the dramatic fluctuations that can be effected upon our butterfly populations by even short-term changes in the weather. In fine seasons the Wall can still be seen, sometimes in good numbers, in Hertfordshire, especially on the Chalk downs, but there are substantial areas of the county, mainly arable and urban, where it is absent or scarce and its future will be very much governed by the vagaries of our climate.

In flight a Wall might be mistaken for one of the small fritillaries or a Comma, but when basking on sunny brickwork, patches of bare ground or low vegetation, its affinities with the other 'browns' are evident, especially in the outline of the wings. Upperwings are dusky-brown near the body, brighter orange on their outer two-thirds, and are crossed by dark brown veins and several wavy lines; they have brown margins. Most conspicuous are the white-pupilled black eyespots, four along the margin of each hindwing and one, quite large, near the apex of each forewing. Beneath, the forewings are paler versions of their uppersides, but the hindwings are beautifully patterned with brown wavy lines across a grey ground to provide superb camouflage when the butterfly is at rest. Towards the margin of each hind underwing is a series of six yellow-and-brown-ringed, white-pupilled, black spots.

As with all the 'browns', Walls form discrete colonies. Their preferred habitat is warm, open, unimproved, flowery grasslands, especially the Chalk downs, with plenty of bare patches amongst the vegetation, but they may be encountered along hedges, road verges, railway embankments and cuttings, on wasteland and around the margins and rides of woodlands. Numbers are seldom high, with usually only a few that consort to feed with the more numerous Ringlets, Gatekeepers and Meadow Browns. Hibernation normally occurs in the larval stage, although some authorities consider that some may overwinter as pupae. The first generation, on the wing from May to early June, is often in noticeably lower numbers than the second, which flies from late July to early September. As noted above, a partial third generation may occur in October during warm seasons. Males may spend long periods perched on patches of bare ground between patrolling flights in search of females. Eggs are deposited, singly or in small batches, low down in sunny sheltered clumps of various grasses including Yorkshire Fog *Holcus lanatus* L., Cocksfoot *Dactylis glomerata* L., Tor Grass *Brachypodium pinnatum* (L.) Beauv. (rare in Hertfordshire), Slender False Brome *B. sylvaticum* (Hudson) Beauv. and Wavy Hair Grass *Deschampsia flexuosa* (L.) Trin. Sites for laying are carefully selected and are usually adjacent to open ground, for example, tracksides or Rabbit scrapes. The well camouflaged green larvae feed nocturnally and finally pupate amongst grass stems.

# Marbled White

*Melanargia galathea* Linnaeus

The Rev. F. H. Knapp – before 1856

PLATE
page 158

Although abundant in Europe, the Marbled White has a distinct ecological limit in southern Britain, and a distinct preference for the unimproved calcareous grasslands of the south-west. The most striking of the 'brown' butterflies, it has never been widespread or really common in Hertfordshire and, like many other species, has been subject to significant population changes associated with climatic fluctuations, agricultural developments and factors affecting the quality of chalk grasslands. It seems fairly safe to assume that Marbled White was scarce and at times absent from Hertfordshire throughout much of the 19th century. Sometime before 1856, the Rev. F. H. Knapp found it at Letchworth, and Newman (1874) notes a sighting at Woodcock Hill, Elstree. Perkins (1878) could only report 'one flying over the playground of the Orphan Asylum' at Watford in 1876. Gibbs (1902) added only a record from Dancer's End near Tring (possibly Buckinghamshire), and in his interesting paper on the Satyrid butterflies (1916) described Marbled White as extinct in the county, although it 'used to occur in the Tring district – from which it has now disappeared, but it is still to be seen in restricted localities

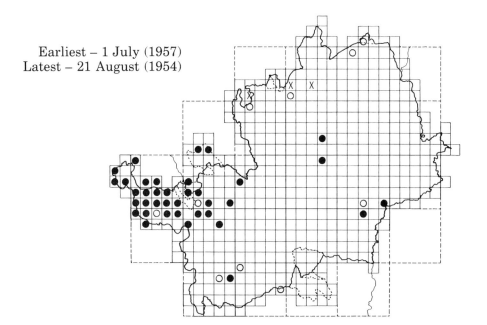

Earliest – 1 July (1957)
Latest – 21 August (1954)

in the Buckinghamshire Chilterns'. Indications are that the species remained in small numbers at Dancer's End until at least the early 1930s. A single Marbled White was seen near Haileybury during the exceptionally hot, dry summer of 1921 and Foster (1934) notes sightings 'of late years' at Therfield Heath, which probably relate to wanderers into the county.

Later data show that Marbled Whites particularly benefit from periods of warmer drier summers and will expand their range if the right habitat is available. During the early part of the 19th century the calcareous grasslands of Hertfordshire, although more extensive, were heavily grazed by both domestic stock and Rabbits. This created a sward which was too short to support sizeable Marbled White colonies, so that there was a real paucity of the species before the poor weather of the later 19th and early part of this century caused virtual local extinction. A combination of warmer summers in the 1940s and relief of grazing pressures saw a substantial, though restricted, spread of Marbled Whites out from their Buckinghamshire strongholds. On 4 July 1943 one was seen near Champneys, just west of Berkhamsted, where, in the next few years further individuals were recorded, and on 28 July 1945 a worn specimen turned up at Aldbury Nowers. The next sighting was at Deacon Hill, on the county boundary with Bedfordshire near Hexton, on 12 July 1947. Bell (1953) noted the continued spread of Marbled White in west Hertfordshire in 1948. From 1948 to 1958 it was found at Jacotts Hill near Whippendell Woods on the western outskirts of Watford. By 1950 a 'fairly strong' colony was established at Aldbury Nowers, and on the nearby Ivinghoe Hills, in Buckinghamshire, no doubt facilitated by the rapid disappearance of Rabbits through myxomatosis, large numbers built up. In his diaries, S. B. Hodgson records large numbers of Marbled Whites on 15 July 1955 over the slopes above Bourn Farm, Northchurch, where they 'swarmed on the patches of musk thistle and abundant knapweed – the females sitting on the flowers and calling or pairing'.

151

Wet, cool summers of the late 1950s and early 1960s drastically reduced Marbled White populations. Many potential sites were lost through agricultural changes, ploughing, and the scrub development that followed the loss of Rabbits from the Chalk downs. Few observations were made during the 1960s and, on 24 July 1966, only a single individual was found at Aldbury Nowers. The better summers which prevailed from 1970 onwards promoted an increase in Marbled White sightings. In 1971 the species reappeared at Aldbury Nowers, in 1972 six individuals were recorded on 30 July and in 1973 it was 'numerous'. From 1977 to date this increase has continued, with a build up of quite good colonies in the better habitats of Hertfordshire and a slow easterly spread to occupy the more suitable sites indicated on the distribution map. In July 1982, a 'tatty' wanderer was found at Stanstead Abbots Gravel Pit; Jacott's Hill near Watford was recolonised in 1983, and other wanderers (although the possibility of escapes cannot be ruled out) were seen at Aston near Stevenage in 1983 and in a meadow by Hoddesdon Lodge on 30 July 1984.

A few apparently suitable sites remain on the Chalk downs in the north of the county around Hexton, near Baldock and at Therfield Heath and it remains to be seen, given good summers, whether or not Marbled White has the ability to spread into these areas, where it has, as far as is known, never really established itself before. Attempts to introduce this butterfly near Pirton in 1975 and to the Weston Hills near Baldock in1981 were unsuccessful, possibly because of inclement weather at the crucial time. But there was evidence that breeding took place (an individual was seen the year after introduction at the latter site) and that the Marbled White is capable of crossing inhospitable countryside (one was found at Norton Common in the centre of Letchworth, two miles to the west of Weston Hills, six days after the introduction there).

Having a single generation, Marbled Whites are on the wing from late June to late August. Even in their slow flapping flight, the black and white chequered upperwings are most distinctive. On the underwings the ground colour varies from white to pale yellow, and the markings are lighter – grey in males and dark green in females. Both sexes have a series of black, blue-centred eyespots near the margins of the hindwings. As with the other 'browns', colonies of the Marbled Whites are discrete and may vary from a few individuals to very large numbers on the more extensive sites. The most favoured habitat is lightly cut or grazed calcareous grassland where the grasses, although not dense, grow reasonably tall. They also frequent open areas in scrub, wide woodland rides even in conifer plantations, road verges and railway embankments, usually preferring sunny sheltered situations. Sometimes large numbers may gather to feed on clumps of taller flowers such as knapweeds, scabious, thistles and brambles.

A mated female perches on tall grass, with wings open and gently pulses her abdomen until an egg emerges; then she flies off, leaving the egg to drop amongst the vegetation, or even to the ground; this egg-laying behaviour is almost certainly not as random as it appears, but involves some form of selection by the female to ensure that eggs are not wasted. Most of the yellow-green larvae are known to feed, at night, on Red Fescue Grass *Festuca rubra* L. but have also been found to feed, at times, on Sheep's Fescue *F. ovina* L., Timothy *Phleum pratense* L. , Cocksfoot *Dactylis glomerata* L. and Tor Grass *Brachypo-dium pinnatum* (L.) Beauv., although Red Fescue appears to be an essential part of their diet, a factor which should be noted with regard to any future conservation efforts or attempts at introductions. Over-wintering pupae are formed in the soil beneath clumps of grasses.

# Grayling

*Hipparchia semele*   Linnaeus

Haileybury Natural Science Society – *c* 1875

Grayling was formerly fairly widespread on sparsely vegetated, dry acid heaths and calcareous grasslands of Britain, although always rather more local away from the coasts and the southern heaths and downs. Many inland colonies have been lost during this century to agriculture, forestry, urban developments and natural succession, as grazing from domestic stock and Rabbits declined. A few references to Grayling in Hertfordshire have been made; none are substantiated with extant specimens, and there may be some reservations regarding the authenticity of some of these. There are strong indications that Grayling was resident in the past at a few select sites in the county and a suspicion that it may have remained at one location, at least, until the 1970s.

PLATE
page 158

About 1875, one specimen (possibly more) was taken by a member of the Haileybury Natural Science Society from the, then, quite extensive heathlands around Hertford Heath. Unfortunately, as with most

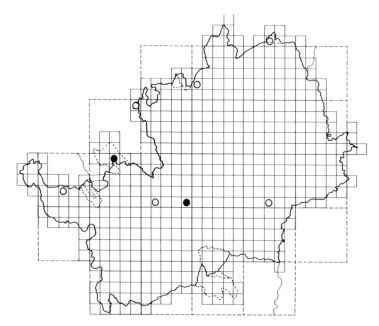

Plate 19 (*Top*)  Silver-washed Fritillary (*Argynnis paphia*) [p. 137]
(*Bottom*)  Marsh Fritillary (*Eurodryas aurinia*) [p. 141]

154

Plate 20 (*Top*)  Speckled Wood (*Pararge aegeria*), [p. 144]
(*Bottom*)  Wall (*Lasiommata megera*) [p. 148]

155

Haileybury material, data labels were not affixed, and it is impossible to be certain of the provenance of extant specimens at the Haileybury Museum. Perkins (1878) notes that he had been informed that this species 'may be taken on the Harpenden road, near Childwick', but had not seen it personally. Gibbs (1902) gives the distinct impression of doubting this record, stating 'this neighbourhood is well known to me but I have failed to find [it] in the locality mentioned by Mr Perkins'. No other 19th century sightings are known.

On 16 June 1912, Ray Palmer, a competent entomologist, took one Grayling and saw another at Wilbury Hill on the outskirts of Letchworth, which with the former wide grassy tracksides of the Icknield Way and a gravel capping to the Chalk would have produced short open grassland congenial to this butterfly. Foster (1934) refers to a sighting 'of late years' by Dr Nash at Therfield Heath, again a possible suitable site, but no further details are available. Hodgson (1943) comments on the report from Aldbury Nowers by Nimmy, published by Foster (1937), as 'vague and unsupported' – [it] 'seems to be the only evidence that this species has ever occurred in the district (west Hertfordshire) or in adjoining areas in Buckinghamshire'.

West (1949), writing on the butterflies of Bedfordshire, discloses that he found 'two battered specimens' in 1944, close to Ravensburgh Castle on the Bedfordshire–Hertfordshire border near Hexton. Another was seen there in 1948, 'flying over previously cultivated ground which bears their favourite flower, Viper's Bugloss (*Echium vulgare* L.) – there is obviously a small colony here, perhaps actually in Hertfordshire'. At that time this site would certainly have been suitable for Grayling, with large areas of gravel-capped, open downs extending into both counties, with short-cropped grassland. Only two further records of this species have been claimed for the county. The first, in the files of the Biological Records Centre at Monks Wood, relates to a possible sighting on the downs about a mile south of Dunstable (just in V C 20) on 1 August 1972, but is without further corroborative evidence. The other was made at Symonshyde Great Wood in 1978 by T. W. Gladwin (personal communication) who noted a specimen in the

> south east corner of the wood where there remained a small remnant of acid heathland on which *calluna* was still well established but there was also a lot of bare ground. I remember the observations well, particularly trying to take photographs with wings in the characteristic totally over-lapped position and the 'keeling' over on one side presumably to take best advantage of the sun. The behavioural comments are a matter of memory, and do not appear in my field notes.

This suggests that Grayling may just have survived in the county at this relict habitat, although there are no earlier references from that area, which was visited by several of the earlier entomologists. The possibility of a wanderer cannot be discounted but the species is not renowned for such behaviour, and a degree of uncertainty must remain over this and the 1972 record. It seems most prudent to assume that Grayling became finally extinct, at least as a resident, in the late 1940s and, in view of the contemporary state of habitats, is unlikely to return.

As indicated above, Grayling is a butterfly of extremely well-drained, generally sparse, unimproved grasslands and heaths, particularly those developed on soils derived from sandstones, gravels, chalk and other limestones, where fine-leaved grasses grow. At very extensive sites large numbers may be found but normally populations are low, and confined to discrete colonies in situations with bare, sheltered 'sunning' spots, often in hollows. Grayling is the largest of our 'browns', with a single generation on the wing from early July to early September. These butterflies nearly always settle on the ground with wings closed so tightly that only the mottled light grey and brown underwings are visible, to give superb camouflage. Usually the wings are angled to face the sun, which may be an adaptation to ensure they receive optimum solar radiation or to reduce the amount of shadow so as to avoid detection by potential predators. If the under forewings are seen they are orange-centred with a grey border and two white-pupilled, black eyespots. Upperwings are light brown with pale yellow bands and two eyespots on the forewings and one near the lower margin of the hindwings.

Between short periods of feeding, Grayling spend much of their time settled in sunny patches on bare ground or amongst sparse vegetation. Here they are difficult to see and, if disturbed, usually only fly a short distance before settling again. Single eggs are laid on the leaves of fine grasses or on nearby debris and twigs. A number of different grasses have been noted as the foodplants of the night-feeding larvae, related to the geological nature of the habitat, the most favoured being fine-leaved Bents *Agrostis* spp. on acid soils and Sheep's Fescue *Festuca ovina* L. on the Chalk. Hibernation takes place in the young larval stage, with a resumption of feeding in the following spring. Full grown in early June, larvae burrow into loose soil and pupate within small silk-lined cells.

# Gatekeeper

*Pyronia tithonus*   Linnaeus

Haileybury Natural Science Society – 1873

Gatekeeper, also frequently referred to as Hedge Brown, has probably always been one of the commonest butterflies of Hertfordshire. It is not quite as ubiquitous as the distribution map might suggest and is generally rather less abundant than its congener, the Meadow Brown. Gibbs (1916) described its chief haunt as 'bramble hedges, where it sometimes appears in swarms, sporting over blossoms', and perhaps its alternative name, Hedge Brown, is more descriptive, as the species has a distinct preference for sites where shrubs are present, such as hedges, lanes, scrub, woodland margins and rides. Although it may be found, sometimes in good numbers, in grasslands, road verges and field edges, really open habitats are avoided and the spread of arable

PLATE
page 159

Plate 21 (*Top*)  Marbled White (*Melanargia galathea*), [p. 150]
(*Bottom*)  Grayling (*Hipparchia semele*) [p. 153]

Plate 22 (*Top*)  Gatekeeper (*Pyronia tithonus*) [p. 157]
(*Bottom*)  Meadow Brown (*Maniola jurtina*) [p. 161]

159

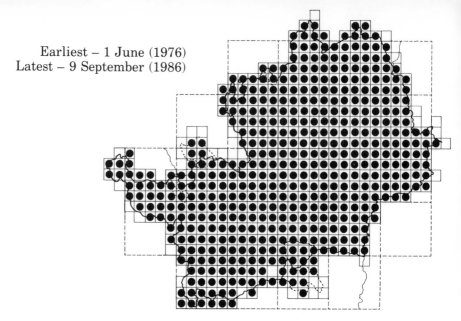

Earliest – 1 June (1976)
Latest – 9 September (1986)

and urban developments in Hertfordshire has reduced populations in many parts. Some compensation has come from the relatively recent overgrowth of shrubs on the now less managed road verges, railway embankments, commons and downs; even small sheltered patches of rough grassland, left in gardens, parks, school grounds and field edges, will attract Gatekeepers, as well as several other butterflies, to breed.

As with most butterflies, there is ample evidence that populations of Gatekeeper are affected by climatic changes, although unfortunately in Hertfordshire no long-term monitoring counts have been maintained and trends have to be ascertained from rather casual observations. Common and widespread in most years, the Gatekeeper usually becomes abundant in fine warm summers. In the early part of summer 1976 this and several other species were present in large numbers, but severely declined as the great drought persisted, desiccating the countryside. Many larvae died of starvation and it took two or three years before populations of Gatekeeper returned to their pre-1976 levels. The fine summers from 1982 to 1984 produced notable increases, which fell again in the miserable summer of 1985, and showed further signs of improvement in 1986.

Interestingly, the prelude to the drought of 1976 brought reports of Gatekeepers on the wing as early as 1 June at Northaw and 6 June at Claypits Meadow south of Bayford, almost six weeks before their normal emergence in mid-July (T. J. James, personal communication). These sightings seem to be amongst the earliest ever appearances of this species in Britain. With a single generation each year, Gatekeepers live in fairly well defined colonies and numbers are at their peak in most years during early August, with a few often remaining into the first days of September. Males are smaller and darker than females and have a distinct dark sex mark across the inner portion of the upper forewings. Both sexes have orange-patched, grey-bordered upperwings, with a double, white-pupilled, black eyespot near the apex of each forewing and one, sometimes more, white spots on the hindwings. Female Meadow Browns, with which this species might be mistaken in southern Britain, are larger and duller with single-pupilled eyespots. Beneath, the forewings of the Gatekeeper are dull orange, with single, double-pupilled eyespots, and the hindwings are mottled brown with, again, one or more white dots.

Eggs are laid, usually singly, on grasses or shrubs in sheltered and lightly shady places; sometimes they are dropped on to grasses in a similar fashion to some of the other 'browns' but always in selected warm situations. Larvae enter hibernation when small and commence feeding in the following spring on a variety of grasses, particularly the fine to medium-leaved Fescues *Festuca* spp., Meadow Grasses *Poa* spp., Bents *Agrostis* spp. and Couch-grass *Elymus repens* (L.) Gould. Full grown larvae may be of two colour forms, grey-green or light brown, with dark longitudinal lines. Pupae are creamy green with dark spots and lines and well hidden low down amongst vegetation.

# Meadow Brown

*Maniola jurtina*   Linnaeus

Haileybury Natural Science Society – 1873

Although numbers rise and fall with changing summer weather and some habitats have been lost to agriculture and other developments, the Meadow Brown remains, as it probably has done since records were kept, Hertfordshire's most abundant butterfly. It forms discrete colonies and does not generally stray very far from breeding areas.

PLATE
page 159

Earliest – 8 May (1887)
Latest – 1 October (1953)

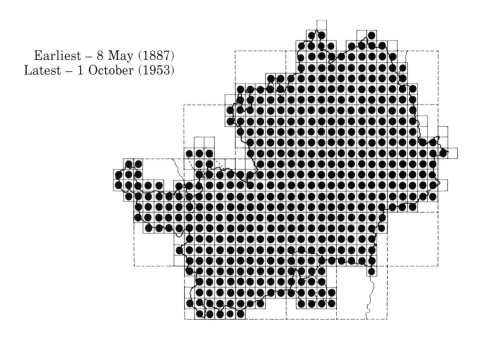

Lower numbers occur in the extensive arable regions and far fewer are seen in urban areas than Small Tortoiseshells or Small Whites. However, almost all woodland clearings, rides and margins, grass-lands, hedgerows, road verges, railway embankments and wastelands will support, sometimes very large, populations. As suggested for some of the other common grassland species, Meadow Browns can be attracted to breed in small areas of tall grass left in gardens and parks.

Fluctuations according to the nature of the seasons closely parallel those of the Gatekeeper and other species. A very early appearance of Meadow Brown was noted by Silvester (1888) at Harpenden on 8 May 1887, in what was to develop into a year of 'prolonged warm weather and long drought', another was reported from Hertford on 4 June in the same year. In 1976 one was seen on 6 June with the Gatekeeper at Claypits Meadow. Perhaps such future occurrences may be used to portend events to come! In most years the first emergence of Meadow Brown does not begin until mid-June, or in late seasons early July. Maximum numbers are usually found during August and a few linger into late September. Even in dull weather many may be on the wing taking nectar from wayside flowers, particularly bram-bles, thistles and knapweeds. The long flight period has led some authorities to speculate that more than one generation occurs; this is refuted by others who maintain that protracted emergences throughout the summer relate to the variable size of larvae when they enter hibernation, large well-fed individuals completing their development sooner.

Female Meadow Browns could be confused with Gatekeepers, but are larger, with a smaller orange patch on each of the brown upper forewings and a single white-pupilled, black eyespot near the apex. Males have dark brown upper forewings, with similar smaller eyespots, which are faintly circled reddish-orange, and may have slight orange patches below these. Upper hindwings of males are dark brown, whilst females are lighter, with a distinct, even lighter, band across the centre. Under hindwings are grey-brown, darker on their inner portions, and under forewings are dark orange with lighter outer portions, dark margins and eyespots similar to those on the upperwings. Many variations of Meadow Brown are known throughout Britain. Like the other grassland 'browns', sometimes females release single eggs whilst perched on grasses and let them drop into the vegetation. Mostly, however, eggs are deposited on the blades of medium-leaved species such as Smooth-stalked Meadow Grass *Poa pratensis* L., which seems to be the principal larval food-plant. After a short period of feeding by day larvae enter hibernation amongst tussocks of grass. In the following spring the bright green larvae resume feeding, but by night, and finally pupate in black-striped chyrsalides hanging from grass stems.

# Small Heath

*Coenonympha pamphilus*   Linnaeus

Haileybury Natural Science Society – 1873

Gibbs (1902), Foster (1937), Waterton (1984) and many other earlier PLATE page 170 recorders regarded Small Heath as a very common species and widely distributed throughout Hertfordshire. Today, it remains fairly common but numbers are almost certainly much reduced and, as the distribution maps shows, it is far from ubiquitous with quite large arable and urban regions where it is apparently absent or very scarce. Many former colonies have been destroyed as grasslands have been cultivated, improved, developed for housing or become rank and over-grown. Frequent small populations are still found at sites on drier soils with short rather sparse vegetation, such as along road verges, railway embankments, hedgerows and woodland rides. In the few remaining unimproved grassland sites in the county larger colonies occur but, even on the Chalk downs that survive, numbers are declining as the height of the sward increases through lack of grazing. A correlation has been detected between annual and long-term fluc-tuations and the summer weather. Numbers crashed after the 1976 drought destroyed a good proportion of summer larvae and it was not until 1979 that populations regained their previous levels. There were slight falls in 1980 and 1981, followed by increases from 1982 to 1984, with particularly strong populations in the fine summer of 1983, and a decline in the poor summer of 1985.

Small Heath usually has two generations a year, sometimes three,

Earliest – 6 May (1957)
Latest – 2 October (1948)

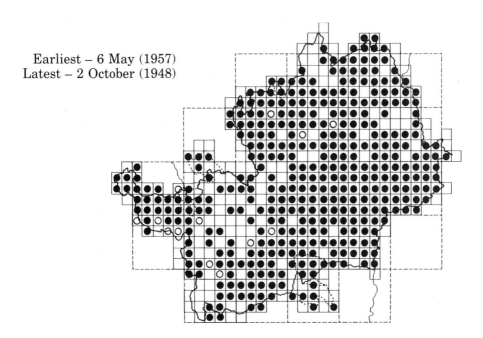

163

and the sequence is complicated as some larvae develop more rapidly than others. It is possible that adults may be found on the wing from mid-May to October, although there are two main periods of abundance, from early June to mid-July and from mid-August to mid-September. Adults are readily differentiated from the other 'browns', skippers and female 'blues' by their small size, wing shape and light brown colouration. They always settle with wings closed. Hind under-wings, which are most frequently seen, are brownish-grey, darker close to the body, with a pale patch near the centre and a faint line of rings concentric to the wing margins. When the under forewing is visible it shows bright orange with grey margins and a conspicuous white-pupilled black eyespot near its apex. Upperwings are orange-brown with dark margins and a single black spot near the apex of each forewing.

Rather sedentary, Small Heaths form close-knit colonies which may contain only a few individuals or, on more extensive and drier grass-land sites, quite large numbers. Sometimes an isolated anthill or part of a dry bank is all that is needed to support a small colony. Adults spend long periods basking on bare earth or low vegetation with closed wings angled toward the sun. They can often be found at roost in the evenings, hanging head down from grass and flower stems. Flight is rapid and erratic as they weave through and above the grasses. A variety of fine-leaved grasses are used for egg-laying and larval feeding, particularly Fescues *Festuca* spp. and Bents *Agrostis* spp., according to the nature of the underlying soils. Diurnal feeders, the green larvae are difficult to find amongst clumps of low growing grasses. As indicated above, larval development is complex. Some develop slowly and enter hibernation in a late larval stage; these resume feeding in the following spring, pupate, and emerge as adults in May and June. More rapid developers pupate, in green, brown-striped chrysalides hanging from grass stems, and emerge as adults in August and September of the same year. Their offspring overwinter as small larvae, to produce adults in the following July, from which the next May to June generation arises. Occasionally a third gener-ation may be produced in exceptionally mild autumns.

# Ringlet

*Aphantopus hyperantus*   Linnaeus

Haileybury Natural Science Society – 1873

PLATE
page 170

The attractive, dusky Ringlet is by no means widespread in Hertford-shire. As the distribution map shows, it is scarce in arable and urban areas, and on the drier soils of the southern portion of the county. Its preferred habitat is damper areas of unimproved meadows, woodland rides and glades, where taller grasses grow. Many such habitats have been destroyed with a resultant loss of some of the larger Ringlet colonies. Good numbers can still be found in the rides and open areas of the Broxbourne Woods and in some of the wooded areas of the Boulder Clay and decalcified Boulder Clay. These butterflies avoid open dry grasslands, but are frequently found in the taller, sheltered grasslands amongst scrub on the lower slopes of the Chalk hills, and are one of the species that have benefited from cessation of grazing and overgrowth of the downs. Small colonies may be met with on road

Earliest – 16 June (1976)
Latest – 27 August (1962)

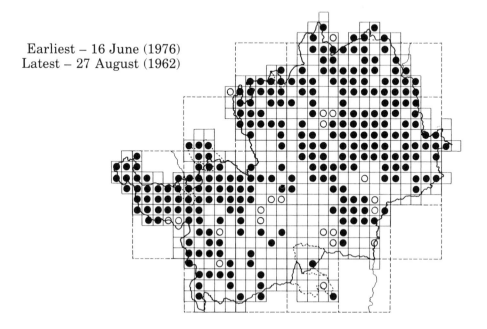

verges, along hedges and trackways in sheltered situations on the damper soils.

Several of the early entomologists commented upon the rather local nature of the Ringlet. Elliman, in Gibbs (1902), observed that near Tring, Ringlet was 'very abundant in most of the woods, but apparently not straying far from them', and the Bishops Stortford Natural History Society (1950) reported it to be 'locally common' and 'confined to certain areas in the Little Hadham district', where, at that time, open damp woods and flowery meadows flourished. Few data are available to evaluate the real declines of Ringlet, although ploughing and improvement of meadows, shading of woods and their rides, and the development of thick scrub have all taken their toll. Reactions to climatic change are essentially similar to those described for the other 'browns', but there is evidence to suggest that Ringlet populations, to some extent, increase after wet seasons. As would be expected, a notable reduction followed the 1976 drought and populations were very high in 1983 and 1984.

Ringlets have a single generation on the wing from early July to mid-August. As with many species there was an early emergence in 1976 and two were seen, by the author, near Tingley Wood, Pirton, on 16 June. Unlike many other species, Ringlets may often be active on cool and overcast days, feeding from various wayside flowers and bramble blossom. The species is named from its distinctive under-wings, each of which has a number of conspicuous white-pupilled, black eyespots, ringed with yellow on a bronzed-brown ground. There are usually five such 'ringlets' on the hindwings and two on the fore-wings. Upperwings are dark velvet-brown, appearing almost black in the males, with, in freshly emerged specimens, distinct white marginal fringes. Upper forewings have two faint black spots near their centres, and upper hindwings two white-pupilled black spots near their trailing margins. In flight the newly emerged Ringlets appear black, but they soon become worn and may be mistaken for male Meadow Browns unless the weaker, fluttering, often apparently hovering flight is noted.

Ringlets are sedentary and their populations, whether large or small, are usually well defined, with a definite relationship between size of site and numbers probably associated with the capacity of the site to support territorial males. Females drop eggs amongst the grasses, but it is uncertain which species the well camouflaged greenish larvae prefer. Often quoted are Annual Meadow Grass *Poa annua* L., Couch-grass *Elymus repens* (L.) Gould, and Tufted Hair-grass *Deschampsia caespitosa* (L.) Beauv.; others are probably also utilised but there is an obvious need for further research. Larvae feed by night and are the overwintering stage of the Ringlet, sometimes breaking hibernation to feed during mild spells. Full grown by early summer, the larvae pupate low down amongst vegetation.

# Milkweed

*Danaus plexippus*   Linnaeus

J. G. Stubbings – 1947

This, the largest butterfly found in Britain, only just 'scrapes' on to the Hertfordshire List on the basis of a single sighting and a matter of yards. Also known as the Monarch, one was seen at Tring Reservoirs in 1947 by J. G. Stubbings, of Ipswich. The record was first published in the July 1948 issue of the *Entomologist* and later by Bell (1952). Stubbings described his exciting find thus, 'During the latter part of August 1947, I was thrilled to see a Milkweed at close quarters. It was resting on flowers in the small area between the two reservoirs (Marsworth and Startops End) by the canal from Bulbourne to Marsworth. I dropped my cardigan over it, but it escaped me'.

Nearly twice the size of a Large White, the Milkweed has most conspicuously coloured orange and black wings. The forewings, in particular, are long and relatively narrow, to facilitate the energy-conserving slow-flapping and gliding flight that is so necessary for long migratory travels. In their native North America, Milkweeds are well known for their annual migrations, sometimes covering thousands of miles, from breeding grounds in the northern states of the USA and Canada to overwinter from Florida to California and down into Mexico. From time to time individuals, sometimes groups, are blown off-course and make a wind-assisted, perhaps sometimes a ship-board, passage of the North Atlantic to make a landfall in Europe. Such vagrants are fairly regular to the south-western seaboard of Britain with occasional occurrences further east. It is also just possible that some sightings may arise from individuals moving north from the Canary Islands and Madeira, where the Milkweed is now established. The absence of the larval foodplants, Milkweeds *Asclepias* spp., and, probably, the wetter climate of western Europe preclude colonisation. Increasingly this species is being captively bred, and some future records may relate to escapes.

# 10

# Conservation and the Future for the Butterflies of Hertfordshire

This book was conceived, and I hope will be used, as an active conservation guide to Hertfordshire's butterflies and their habitats. Thanks to the enthusiasm and efforts of many people, we now have most of the necessary facts regarding distribution, rarity, species requirements and important habitats to select priorities that will enable the various conservation organisations in the county to make a start. Nothing can be done about our climate, although by assisting population increases of the scarcer species the effects of climatic extremes may be reduced. We have seen how the neglect of traditional land uses has resulted in the loss of our historical countryside. Records clearly show that the more varied landscape before the 1940s held a richer wildlife, with a greater number of species and higher populations of butterflies. There have always been changes, but the pace and scale of change in the last forty years or so have been so rapid and widespread that damage is almost certainly irrevocable. Some agricultural statistics suggest that a proportion of the relatively newly created arable and improved lands is superfluous, as some of their products are wasted or stockpiled. For what? Many of the newer plantations, which replaced our historic woodlands, have no market for their timber. Yet there are still pressures to cultivate marginal land, fell or replace old woods, plough or improve ancient grasslands, remove hedges or trackways, all of which further reduce, isolate and fragment the better habitats for wildlife.

Farmers, landowners and local authorities largely hold the key to the fate of what remains of our natural heritage. They can, perhaps, be swayed by meaningful public and political opinion, or future approaches, to adopt more sensitive attitudes, to enter into management agreements or to establish nature reserves to protect rare species and the best sites. Some headway is already being made but there is a long way to go. Many of those that own and tend the land are very aware of conservation problems and might welcome ongoing liaison with a conservation advisory group. If this is achieved then those responsible for future conservation measures must ensure that policies and decisions are well founded, and that, above all, management is well executed, to maintain long-term viable populations and habitats. It is not easy to replicate historic habitats nor to create the exacting requirements of certain species. Some of the practical problems are great, particularly in ensuring continuity of management of sites and providing the necessary manpower to accomplish this, but these should not be insoluble if the commitment is there. Mis- or delayed manage-

Figure 10.1 *Hertfordshire's top two sites are a mixture of woodland and Chalk down-land. Continuing management is necessary if the rarer butterflies are to remain. (Tingley Wood)*

ment may be devastating to some butterflies which exist in small numbers within restricted sites.

There is a great need for a wider appreciation of the history of our landscape, the development and maintenance of habitats, and the interactions between species. Further research and education are vital at all levels. For example, the clearance of scrub at a particular site to encourage certain species of butterflies might destroy other much rarer species of plants or animals; tree-planting on a village green, road verge or field margin could well eliminate many local butterflies, as can over-mowing in the search for 'neatness'. It would therefore be beneficial for future butterfly conservation, at least, to be co-ordinated, controlled and monitored through one of the existing conservation organisations, or by a group, established – as soon as possible for this purpose – with various representations from other bodies.

From all the butterfly records received fron Hertfordshire between 1970 and 1986 'a league table' has been drawn up of relative abundance, and the current status of species is shown in Table 10.1. Only twenty-one species, including the migrants Red Admiral and Painted Lady, are common or reasonably widespread, and between them these accounted for over 90 per cent of all observations made. Several of those categorised as common residents are threatened with significant reductions as their semi-natural grassland habitats are further degraded. Speckled Wood, Marbled White and White Admiral have shown recent increases in their respective populations and ranges, but these may be short-lived. Further suitable sites for colonisation are limited and, as past experience has shown, a series of poor summers could dramatically reduce numbers and cause local extinctions. It is within this category of restricted resident butterflies that real considerations for conservation should begin. The presence of one or more of those species listed will, in most instances, indicate a site of some importance. There is scope for much future work on data collected so far to identify all potentially good sites. Unfortunately space does not permit the inclusion of a full list here, but all original

169

Plate 23 (*Top*) Small Heath (*Coenonympha pamphilus*) [p. 163]
(*Bottom*) Ringlet (*Aphantopus hyperantus*) [p. 164]

170

TABLE 10.1  The status of Hertfordshire's butterflies, from records 1970–1986

The species are listed within the columns in descending order of abundance of records received

| Common and widespread residents | Common residents | Restricted residents | Rare residents | Very rare residents | Migrants | Vagrants | Former residents, now extinct |
|---|---|---|---|---|---|---|---|
| Meadow Brown | Common Blue | Speckled Wood | Small Blue | Brown Hairstreak | Red Admiral | Camberwell Beauty | Wood White |
| Small Tortoiseshell | Large Skipper | *Purple Hairstreak | Chalkhill Blue | Purple Emperor | Painted Lady | Large Tortoiseshell | High Brown Fritillary |
| Small White | Small Heath | Brown Argus | Dark Green Fritillary | | ‡Clouded Yellow | Queen of Spain Fritillary | Pearl-bordered Fritillary |
| Peacock | Wall | White-letter Hairstreak | Silver-washed Fritillary | | | Pale Clouded Yellow | |
| Gatekeeper | *Essex Skipper | White Admiral | Duke of Burgundy | | | Grayling | |
| Large White | Ringlet | Marbled White | | | | | |
| Green-veined White | Holly Blue | Dingy Skipper | | | | | |
| Orange Tip | Small Copper | Grizzled Skipper | | | | | |
| Comma | | Green Hairstreak | | | | | |
| Small Skipper | | | | | | | |
| Brimstone | | | | | | | |
| *Proportion of records* 65% | 24% | 4% | less than 1% | less than 1% | 6% | less than 1% | less than 1% |

*probably under-recorded

‡over 75% of all Clouded Yellow records were made in 1983

171

Figure 10.2 *Patmore Heath with its acid grassland and surrounding woods is the richest area for butterflies in the north-eastern part of Hertfordshire*

lists and data will be maintained in the files of North Hertfordshire Museums Natural History Department (in Baldock) for ongoing detailed researches.

There is a very real crisis facing Hertfordshire's seven most endangered resident butterflies and local extinctions are serious possibilities in the not too distant future. Small Blue occurs at no more than ten sites, all with rather small populations; only one of these, a County Trust nature reserve, is regularly managed for its butterflies. Duke of Burgundy is restricted, in low numbers, to possibly just a single site; it was found at a County Trust nature reserve, but there have been no records made there since 1979. Therfield Heath, a Local Nature Reserve, receiving some management from the County Trust, suppoorts the only remaining breeding colonies of the Chalkhill Blue in Hertfordshire, but even there numbers are perilously low, and the future viability of this beautiful butterfly is most uncertain. Dark Green and Silver-washed Fritillaries are strong-winged and mobile, so that a good majority of recent sightings may relate to wanderers; breeding is difficult to prove, but is suspected from just a few locations. Brown Hairstreak and Purple Emperor, both species of ancient semi-natural woodland complexes, are without doubt our most elusive and, probably, rarest resident butterflies. Both require prompt, detailed investigations to elucidate the true extent of their populations and conservation requirements. In the species accounts the vulnerability of butterflies with low populations has been detailed. Three species that were former residents in Hertfordshire, Wood White, High Brown Fritillary and Pearl-bordered Fritillary, have become extinct since 1970, but might well have been saved if appropriate measures had been taken to safeguard their habitats. Action must be taken to prevent the loss of any further species.

Hertfordshire's twenty-five most important areas for butterflies, based upon post-1970 records, are shown on the end maps and listed in Table 10.2, with a note of the total number of species recorded in the relevant tetrads. Those areas, or sites, that have some form of designated protection are annotated thus: Site of Special Scientific Interest (SSSI), Local Nature Reserve (LNR), Hertfordshire and

Middlesex Wildlife Trust nature reserve (Trust NR). Most of the important sites are only fragments of formerly extensive areas and often isolated. Half of these, including the top two (although these are being considered for SSSI status), are without any form of designated protection at the time of writing. Aldbury Nowers, the prime site, requires urgent conservation management if several of its more interesting species are to survive encroaching scrub. The varied complex of downland and wood at Highdown near Pirton is fortunately under

TABLE 10.2 *The twenty-five most important areas for butterflies in Hertfordshire*

| Name of area | Number of species recorded in relevant tetrad(s) | Designation |
|---|---|---|
| Aldbury Nowers | 34 | |
| Highdown, Pirton | 32 | |
| Whippendell Woods/Jacott's Hill | 30 | part SSSI |
| Knebworth Woods | 29 | SSSI |
| Balls Wood/Hertford Heath | 29 | part SSSI |
| Ashridge/Berkhamsted Common | 29 | part SSSI |
| Hexton/Lilley Hoo | 28 | includes Trust NR |
| Bayfordbury | 28 | |
| Broxbourne Woods/Wormley Wood | 28 | part SSSI |
| Hudnall Common/ Ravensdell Wood | 28 | |
| Tewin/Bramfield | 28 | |
| Therfield Heath | 27 | LNR and SSSI; part Trust NR |
| Bricket Wood | 27 | SSSI |
| Tring Reservoirs | 27 | part SSSI |
| Ayot/Brocket | 26 | |
| Aston/Benington | 26 | includes Trust NR |
| Radlett | 26 | |
| Ickleford | 25 | |
| Hitch Wood | 25 | |
| Sherrardspark Wood | 25 | SSSI |
| Bulbourne | 25 | |
| High Scrubs/Tring Park | 25 | part SSSI |
| Hook Wood/Potters Bar | 24 | |
| Weston Hills | 24 | |
| Patmore Heath | 24 | SSSI; Trust NR |

the control of a sympathetic landowner and, might, because of its proximity to the Knocking Hoe National Nature Reserve, just over the border in Bedfordshire, become more interesting. Many of the other top sites have long been known to naturalists and several, at least in part, have been afforded some degree of protection. However, it is apparent that few have long-term management regimes directed towards the conservation of their butterflies.

As would be expected, most of the better areas for butterflies are found in the south and west of the county, the cooler, damper and now intensively cultivated regions in the north and east being, as they probably have for a long time, less suitable for the existence and spread of many species. Also of interest is the general area, mainly on sands and gravels, running from south-east to north-west across the middle of the county. This shows up quite distinctly in the distribution of many species, and reflects the fact that it has generally poorer soils that support better mixtures of surviving semi-natural habitats. The list of important sites should not be regarded as definitive, for there are still a few areas that are probably under-recorded and might well repay further field investigations. Such detailed studies are responsible for the high species-counts from areas that formerly seemed unpromising at Radlett and Potters Bar. As noted above, space does not permit the tabulation of all the interesting areas discovered so far. Some indication of these can be ascertained by examination of the species-recorded-per-tetrad map (Fig. 7.1 on p. 28) and the species-distribution maps, or by consultation of the original data held at North Hertfordshire Museums. It cannot be over-emphasised that resolute action must be taken *now* to safeguard the future of Hertfordshire's butterflies and their habitats. Rumours of some drastic changes in the countryside are currently growing, and future British farming may, perhaps, be put under pressure to reduce production of certain crops and animals. If such rumours become reality, what will happen? Will there be vast tracts of land available for speculative development? How will the future of what remains of our countryside and its wildlife be affected? The implications and possible solutions to such questions need to be looked at, with some urgency, by all who have an interest in wildlife, before it is too late.

A fundamental, yet most important, adjunct to future conservation must be the continued study and recording of our butterflies, especially those species most at risk. Recorders are urged to maintain a flow of information to the biological data banks at North Hertfordshire and St Albans Museums (*see* Appendix 1), from where it will be passed to those responsible for record-collation, interpretation and conservation activities. There is a need for detailed studies of sites, to determine their historical development, current structure, diversity of plants and animals, and conservation potential. More could be learned of the local ecological requirements of many species of butterflies and how their populations might be increased. In the species accounts, several rueful references are made to the lack of long-term surveys, particularly with many quite common butterflies. At some of the key sites, or even in other areas, periodic counts associated with the national Butterfly

Monitoring Scheme, organised by the Institute of Terrestrial Ecology, should be undertaken. This is a fairly straightforward exercise, requiring regular visits to a site throughout the butterfly 'season' to make sample counts, but it provides vital data on population changes and can give early warning of declines. Recording, of all aspects of natural history, and conservation activities should be one of the prime objectives of our natural history societies. Much of the success of the Butterfly Survey, one of the most comprehensive wildlife studies ever carried out in Hertfordshire, is owed to the fact that many people took part and even casual sightings have proved valuable. All one needs to start is an inexpensive notebook and pen to note down observations, including location, date and any other details. Periodically lists can then be submitted to the data banks to add to the growing knowledge of the county's natural history. Increased expertise and enjoyment can be gained by joining one or more of the natural history and conser-vation groups (listed in Appendix 1). The future conservation of our butterflies, their habitats, and other wildlife will only succeed with unified, strong and determined efforts, and, importantly, financial support to facilitate the acquisition of nature reserves and the necessary remedial or ongoing management of sites.

Like charity, conservation can begin at home. Gardens, parks and churchyards are readily made more attractive for butterflies. Road verges, greens and playing fields are quite easily enhanced by regu-lating management in small areas, if the will, interest and commit-ment is there. Hertfordshire County Council is already experimenting with the creation of interesting habitats on stretches of certain new road verges. More consideration might also be given to the treatment of many existing verges which support, in some regions, the last relicts of formerly extensive habitats, but remain quite important for insects.

Figure 10.3 *Active conservation management will be vital to the survival of many butterflies*

Habitats can be created or resuscitated from the most unpromising land. However, it should not be automatically assumed that the more important sites will be looked after and every effort should be made to ensure that some priority is given to them. With the development, of correct and lasting site-management regimes consideration may then be able to be given to the re-introduction or establishment of scarce species, although the advice and approval of the Nature Conservancy Council (*see* Appendix 1) should be sought before any such attempts are made. Undocumented releases and thoughtless introductions can be very damaging to monitoring programmes and habitat assessments for conservation proposals and priorities.

Butterfly-collecting is an emotive issue. Little of scientific value is to be gained from such activities in Hertfordshire. Most of the rarer species, especially those living in small colonies, could well be exterminated by even small-scale collecting. None of the following – Brown Hairstreak, Small Blue, Chalkhill Blue, Duke of Burgundy, Purple Emperor, Dark Green Fritillary, Silver-Washed Fritillary – or any other rare or locally scarce species should, under any circumstances, be collected in the county. Anyone who does feel the need to collect should pay due attention to the guidelines set out in *A Code for Insect Collecting* produced by the Joint Committee for the Conservation of British Insects.

Because of the available facts, I have had to describe a rather depressing picture of Hertfordshire's butterflies, with frequent references to local extinctions and declines, habitat loss and deterioration, and, sometimes, lack of available detailed information. There are some brighter spots, hopefully not temporary, such as the recent increases and spread of a few species. I have attempted to show the importance of continued studies, for butterflies are, in most instances, easily seen monitors of subtle environmental disturbances and may be used as early indicators forewarning changes that affect other forms of wildlife and, perhaps, ultimately ourselves. Some indications are given of those species most in danger of disappearing from the Hertfordshire countryside and some of the remedial measures required to prevent this. Amongst the references listed are several authoritative works relating to principles and techniques for practical butterfly-conservation and habitat management. We now have the facts and must ensure that a better future is secured for the butterflies of Hertfordshire.

# Appendices

# Appendix 1

*Organisations concerned with butterfly recording and conservation*

Because officers and addresses of some organisations are subject to change they are omitted from the list below. The reader is best referred to local museums and libraries for up to date information on these, especially where

| | |
|---|---|
| Natural History Department | Keeper of Natural History |
| North Hertfordshire Museums | City Museum |
| Old Fire Station | Hatfield Road |
| Baldock | St Albans |
| Herts. | Herts. |
| SG7 6AR | AL1 3RR |
| *Telephone* Baldock (0462) 894352 | *Telephone* St Albans (0727) 56679 |

the major data files for Hertfordshire's flora, fauna and important natural history sites are maintained in the respective North and South Hertfordshire Biological Records Centres.

**Hertfordshire Natural History Society** is the premier organisation for the study of natural history in the county. It organises a series of lectures and field meetings, promotes surveys and annually publishes the *Transactions*, which contains papers and articles related to all aspects of the natural sciences in Hertfordshire.

**London Natural History Society**, whose area encompasses a twenty-mile radius of St Paul's Cathedral including part of southern Hertfordshire, encourages fieldwork, research and publication of information relating to that region.

**The British Naturalists' Association** seeks 'to further the education of the general public in the study of natural history' and has an active Hertfordshire Branch which organises a full programme of meetings with many field excursions to all parts of the county.

Local natural history societies are based at Letchworth, Welwyn, Bishops Stortford and Cheshunt. All have programmes, covering many aspects of wildlife, with indoor and outdoor meetings, and often link with other organisations in the furtherance of studies and conservation activities.

**The Nature Conservancy Council** is the government body which promotes nature conservation in Great Britain. It gives advice on nature conservation to government and all whose activities affect our wildlife and wild places. It selects, establishes and manages National Nature Reserves and is responsible for the designation of Sites of Special Scientific Interest. The Assistant Regional Officer is based at

Archway House
7, Eastcheap
Letchworth
Herts.
SG6 3DC
*Telephone* Letchworth (0462) 675830

**The Hertfordshire and Middlesex Wildlife Trust** is the major voluntary wildlife conservation organisation for the county. To date, it owns or manages over forty nature reserves and promotes a wide range of related events and activities. Several local groups have been established to support and publicise the aims of the Trust through field excursions, fund-raising, conservation tasks, nature reserve open days, talks and filmshows on wildlife and surveys. The Trust can be contacted at

Grebe House
St Michaels Street
St Albans
Herts.
AL3 4SN
*Telephone* St Albans (0727) 58901

**WATCH** is a national organisation with many county and local branches associated with the county wildlife conservation Trusts. Its aims are to encourage and teach children, between the ages of eight and fifteen, the value and beauty of the environment. In Hertfordshire there are several local groups which organise exciting and varied programmes of indoor and outdoor activities, including quite important studies of local and national interest. Further information is available from

WATCH (Herts and Middx Organiser)
Hudnall Park Environmental Studies Centre
Little Gaddesden
Berkhamsted
Herts.
*Telephone*
Little Gaddesden (9584) 3400

WATCH Trust for Environmental Education Ltd
22, The Green
Nettleham
Lincoln
LN2 2NR
*Telephone* Lincoln (0522) 752326

**The British Butterfly Conservation Society** was established to protect our butterflies through increased public awareness, conservation of important sites and declining species, and the encouragement of scientific research and butterfly breeding. It seeks to form branches throughout the country. Its head office is at

Tudor House
Quorn
Leics.
LE12 8AD

**The Amateur Entomologists' Society** was founded in 1935 for the promotion of entomological knowledge through meetings, exhibitions and its bulletins. It has a keen interest in encouraging beginners and is based at

355 Hounslow Road
Hanworth
Feltham
Middx
TW13 5JH

Both the Biological Records Centre and the Butterfly Monitoring Scheme are based at

The Institute of Terrestrial Ecology
Monks Wood Experimental Station
Abbots Ripton
Huntingdon
Cambs.
PE17 2LS
*Telephone* Abbots Ripton (04873) 381

and are part of the Natural Environmental Research Council which specialises in detailed ecological research and gives impartial advice to all enquirers. Essential research is financed by the government, and both private and public sector customers commission specific research programmes. Both departments are concerned with the collection, collation and interpretation of butterfly records on a national scale and rely heavily upon input from regional and local studies by amateurs.

**The Farming and Wildlife Advisory Group** has a branch in Hertfordshire and its objectives are 'to develop liaison between farming and conservation interests at a local level with a view to providing practical advice on the conservation of wildlife and landscape to farmers'. Study visits, advice and assistance in the preparation of conservation schemes are free from the local FWAG officer, who can be contacted at

AIDAS
Sovereign House
Hale Road
Hertford
SG13 8EB
*Telephone* Hertford (0992) 553911

Hertfordshire County Council's Planning Department operates a **Country-side Management Service**, which carries out practical conservation work in the county to care for the landscape and its wildlife habitats. It offers opportunities for volunteers to join with its professional work force and welcomes requests for advice and assistance in local conservation and amenity projects. For further information contact

The Countryside Management Service
County Planning Department
County Hall
Hertford
SG13 8DN
*Telephone* Hertford (0992) 555250

# Appendix 2

## *Tetrad Mapping*

Mapping species-distribution on a tetrad basis has become an accepted and important part of natural history documentation. It eases the critical determination of those areas occupied by the diversity of flora and fauna and facilitates comparisons between the various species and the distribution of species with various 'mappable' environmental factors such as geology and soils, local climatic variations, vegetation types, topographical features and land uses.

All the maps showing tetrads in this book have a solid base outline denoting the present boundaries of Hertfordshire. Old boundaries are indicated by dotted lines. The larger squares are 10km x 10km which relates to the areas covered by individual modern Ordnance Survey 1 : 25000 (2½″ : 1 mile) maps, each designated by the standard Ornance Survey notation, SP 90, SP 91, TQ 09, TL 00, etc. (*See* Figure 7.2 page 29). Within each of these 10km squares are twenty-five 2km squares, called tetrads, which are the basic units adopted for mapping in most of the county's wildlife studies. Each tetrad is given a letter, from A to Z omitting O (*see* inset Figure 7.2), which uniquely identifies it, successive letters referring to tetrads with larger grid reference numbers. Starting in the south-west corner of a 10km square, A is 00, B is 02, and so on until Z, which is 88. Different symbols may be mapped into the tetrads to show various classes of records, for example those chosen to illustrate the butterfly-distribution maps.

Places and sites can be definitively referenced for efficient index systems, particularly when computerised, and mapping can be achieved without too much background clutter, for example Norton Common, Letchworth, is in tetrad TL 23B and Patmore Heath near Albury is in TL 42M. Further suffixes can be used for even finer detail. There are some drawbacks in that some site names, especially those accompanying old records or which are locally derived, may not be found on or are inconsistent with modern maps. Also the symbols used for the tetrad record rarely give any indication of abundance – they may relate to one or a thousand sightings, and many sites overlap tetrad boundaries which, with some records, could lead to indecision over where to place the symbol. To avoid such problems (for tetrad maps should not be regarded as the definitive records) data files must be maintained with full and detailed information, such as numbers seen, dates of observations, full details and grid references of locations, recorder's name, and other relevant details.

# Appendix 3

*A Gazetteer of Locations Mentioned in the Text, with Tetrad Notations*

Where a location falls into more than one tetrad, the notation is for that containing the greater proportion. Sites marked * are not named on modern Ordnance Survey 1 : 25000 maps.

| | | | |
|---|---|---|---|
| Albury | TL 42H | (Forestry Commission | |
| Aldbury | SP 91R | plantations) | |
| *Aldbury Downs | SP 91L | Brambles Wood | TL 30J |
| Aldbury Nowers | SP 91L | *Brickendon Common | TL 30I |
| Aldenham Park | TQ 19T | Bricket Wood | TL 10F |
| Apsley End | TL 00S | Brights Hill | TL 21Y |
| Ardeley | TL 32D | Broad Riding Wood | TL 30N |
| Ashridge (=Ashridge | SP 91W | Brocket Park | TL 21B |
| Park) | | *Brown's Lane, Tring | SP 91F |
| *Ashridge Common | SP 91Q, | *Broxbournebury Gravel | TL 30N |
| (probably includes | R, V | Pit | |
| Ashridge Park, Aldbury | and W | *Broxbourne Common | TL 30N |
| Common and | | *Broxbourne Woods | TL 30I, |
| Berkhamsted Common) | | (a complex of woods | J, N |
| Aston | TL 22R | between Hoddesdon and | and P |
| Astonbury Wood | TL 22Q | Brickendon including | |
| Ashwell | TL 23U | Brambles Wood, Broad | |
| *Ashwell Quarries Nature | TL 23P | Riding Wood, | |
| Reserve | | Broxbourne Wood, | |
| Ayot Green | TL 21H | Cowheath Wood, | |
| Ayot St Peter | TL 21C | Highfield Wood, | |
| *Ayot Way (disused | TL 21C | Hoddesdonpark Wood | |
| railway line) | | and others) | |
| | | Bulbourne | SP 91G |
| Baldock | TL 23M | Buntingford | TL 32U |
| Balls Wood | TL 31K | *Burleigh Heath | TL 22G |
| Barton Hills, Beds | TL 02Z | *Burleigh Meadow | TL 22G |
| Barwick | TL 31Z | Bury Green | TL 42K |
| Bayford | TL 30E | Bushey | TQ 19H |
| *Beech Wood, Barnet | TQ 29T | | |
| (= wood near Beech Hill | | Camfield Place | TL 20T |
| Lake) | | *Carpenders | TQ 19G |
| Berkhamsted | SP 90Y | (= Carpenders Park) | |
| Berkhamsted Common | SP 91V | Champneys | SP 90P |
| Birchanger Wood | TL 52B | Chandlers Cross | TQ 09U |
| Bishops Stortford | TL 42V | Charlton | TL 12U |
| Bloodhounds Wood | TL 42R | *Chesfield (= Chesfield | TL 22N |
| Borehamwood | TQ 19Y | Park) | |
| *Bourn Farm, | SP 90T | Cheshunt | TL 30L |
| Northchurch | | *Childwick (= Childwick | TL 11K |
| *Bourne Gutter | TL 00H | Green) | |
| Bovingdon | TL 00B | Chipperfield | TL 00K |
| Boxmoor | TL 00N | Chpperfield Common | TL 00K |
| Box Wood | TL 22T | Chiswellgreen | TL 10H |
| Bramfield | TL 21X | Chorleywood | TQ 19I |
| *Bramfield Woods | TL 21Y | *Claypits Meadow | TL 30D |

| | |
|---|---|
| Clothall | TL 23Q |
| Codicote | TL 21E |
| Colney Heath | TL 10Y |
| Commonwood Common | TL 00K |
| Cowheath Wood | TL 30I |
| Crews Hill | TL 30A |
| Crouch Green | TL 22A |
| *Croxley Common Moor (=Common Moor) | TQ 09X |
| Cuffley | TL 30B |
| Dancersend (= Dancer's End), Bucks. | SP 90E |
| Datchworth | TL 21U |
| Deacon Hill, Beds. | TL 12J |
| Digswell | TL 21H |
| Drayton Beauchamp, Bucks. | SP 81W |
| Dunstable, Beds | TL 02A and F |
| East Barnet | TQ 29S |
| East Hyde, Beds. | TL 11I |
| Essendon | TL 20U |
| Farnham, Essex | TL 42S |
| Fishers Green | TL 22I |
| Flaunden | TL 00A |
| Frithsden Beeches | SP 91V |
| *Fulling Mill | TL 21I |
| *Furze Wood (= The Furze Field) | TL 20P |
| Goldings Wood | TL 31K |
| Goldingtons | TQ 09J |
| Graveley | TL 22I |
| Great Gaddesden | TL 01F |
| Great Hormead | TL 43A |
| Great Hormead Park | TL 42E |
| Grove Wood | SP 90E |
| *Hadley Woods (= Hadley Common) | TQ 29N |
| *Haileybury (= Haileybury College and surrounding area) | TL 31K |
| Harmergreen Wood | TL 21N |
| Harpenden | TL 11H |
| Harpenden Common | TL 11G |
| Hastoe Hill | SP 90E |
| Hatfield | TL 20J |
| Hatfield Park | TL 20N |
| Hemel Hempstead | TL 00N, S and T |
| Hertford | TL 31B and G |
| Hertford Heath | TL 31K |
| Hexton | TL 13A |
| *Hexton Chalk Pit | TL 12E |
| Highdown | TL 13K |
| High Scrubs | SP 90J |
| Hilfield Lane | TQ 19N |
| *Hillend (= Hillend Farm) | TL 12W |
| Hitchin | TL 12Z |
| Hitch Wood | TL 12W |
| Hockeridge Wood, Bucks. | SP 90T |
| Hoddesdon | TL 30U |
| Hoddesdon Lodge | TL 30P |
| Hoddesdonpark Wood | TL 30P |
| Hoggates Wood | TL 42R |
| Holwell | TL 13R |
| Hook Wood | TL 20Q |
| Hudnall Common | TL 01B |
| *Hudnall Park | TL 01B |
| Ickleford | TL 13V |
| Incombe Hole, Bucks. | SP 91M |
| Ivinghoe Hills, Bucks. | SP 91S and T |
| Jacott's Hill | TQ 09Y |
| Kings Langley | TL 00R |
| Knebworth | TL 22K |
| *Knebworth Great Wood (= Newton Wood) | TL 22G |
| *Knebworth Woods (includes Newton Wood, Cowleys Corner Wood, Wintergreen Wood, Burleigh Grove, The Firs, Watery Grove and Norton Green) | TL 22F and G |
| *Knocking Hoe National Nature Reserve, Beds. | TL 13F |
| Langley | TL 22B |
| Ledgeside Plantation | TL 22P |
| Letchworth | TL 23A, B, F and G |
| *Letchworth Park (probably Letchworth Hall) | TL 23A |
| Lilley | TL 12D |
| Lilley Hoo | TL 12I and J |
| Little Hadham | TL 42L |
| Lockleys Wood | TL 21M |
| Longcroft Lane, Tring | SP 90E |
| *Long Green | TL 00D |
| *Long Meadow | TL 42Q |
| Mardley Heath | TL 21P |
| *Marsworth Reservoir, mainly in Bucks. | SP 91G |

| | | | |
|---|---|---|---|
| Meesden | TL 43G | St John's Wood | TL 32C |
| Much Hadham | TL 41J | Sallow Copse, Bucks. | SP 91R |
| *Mimms, Mymms | TL 20F | Sandon | TL 33H |
| (= South Mimms) | | Sandridge | TL 11Q |
| *Mymms Park (= North | TL 20C | Sawtrees Wood | TL 31Z |
| Mymms Park) | | Sherrardspark Wood | TL 21G |
| New Barnet | TQ 29N | Southgate | TQ 29X |
| | and S | South Mimms | TL 20F |
| Ninesprings, Purwell | TL 22E | *Stagenhoe Lane | TL 12W |
| Nomansland Common | TL 11R | Stags End | TL 01Q |
| Northaw | TL 20W | Standon | TL 32W |
| Northaw Great Wood | TL 20X | *Stanstead Abbots Gravel | TL 31V |
| Northchurch | SP 90U | Pit | |
| Northey Wood | TL 43B | *Startops End Reservoir, | SP 91B |
| Norton Common | TL 23B | mainly in Bucks. | |
| Norton Green | TL 22G | Stevenage (Old Town) | TL 22H |
| Nuthampstead | TL 43C | Stocking Plantations | TL 42K |
| Oaklands | TL 10Y | (= Stocking Wood | and Q |
| Odsey, Cambs. | TL 23Z | Plantation and nearby | |
| Oughtonhead Common | TL 13Q | woods) | |
| Oxbury Wood | TL 43K | Stubbings Wood | SP 91A |
| Oxhey Woods | TQ 19B | Studham, Beds | TL 01H |
| | | Symonshyde Great Wood | TL 11V |
| Parkhill Farm | SP 91L | Tewin | TL 21S |
| Patmore Hall Wood | TL 42N | *The Dell, Cuffley | TL 20W |
| Patmore Heath | TL 42M | The Frythe, Welwyn | TL 21H |
| *Pegsdon Hills (includes | TL 12E | Therfield Heath | TL 33J, |
| Telegraph Hill, Noon | and J | | TL 34G |
| Hill and Deacon Hill) | | | and K |
| Pirton | TL 13K | The Node, Codicote | TL 22A |
| Pitstone Hill, Bucks. | SP 91M | The Roughs | TL 20N |
| Plashes Wood | TL 32V | Thorley | TL 41U |
| Potten End | TL 00E | Thorley Wood | TL 41Z |
| Potters Bar | TL 20K | Tingley Field Plantation, | TL 13F |
| | and Q | Beds. | |
| Potterscrouch | TL 10C | Tingley Wood | TL 13F |
| Prae Wood | TL 10I | Tring | SP 91F |
| Preston | TL 12S | Tring Park | SP 91F |
| *Purwell | TL 22E | *Tring Reservoirs, mainly | SP 91B |
| Radlett | TQ 19P | in Bucks. | and G |
| | and U | Tring Station | SP 91L |
| Ravensburgh Castle | TL 02Z | Wain Wood | TL 12S |
| Ravensdell Wood, Beds. | TL 01C | Walkern | TL 22Y |
| Redbourn | TL 11B | Ware | TL 31M |
| Rickmansworth | TQ 09M | | and S |
| | and S | Watery Grove | TL 22G |
| Roman Road (= Elbow | TL 31K | Watford | TQ 09X |
| Lane) | | | Y, Z; |
| Rothamsted | TL 11G | | TQ 19D |
| Roughdown Common | TL 00M | | and E |
| Royston | TL 34K | Watton-at-Stone | TL 31E |
| St Albans | TL 10N, | Well Wood | TL 20R |
| | P, T | Welwyn | TL 21I |
| | and U | Welwyn Garden City | TL 21G |
| | | | and L |

| | | | |
|---|---|---|---|
| Westmill | TL 32T | Widford | TL 41C |
| Weston Hills | TL 23L | Wilbury Hill | TL 23B |
| Wiggington | SP 91F | Willian | TL 23F |
| Wheathampstead | TL 11S | Wintergreen Wood | TL 22F |
| Whempstead | TL 32A | Woodcock Hill, Elstree | TQ 19X |
| Whippendell Wood | TQ 09U | Wormley Wood | TL 30H |
| Whitwell | TL 12V | | |

# Bibliography

ARNOLD, V. W. and MANNING, D. V. (1983) *A Provisional Check List of the Butterflies and Moths of Bedfordshire*, Bedfordshire Natural History Society, Bedford.

BARRAUD, P. J. (1903) Notes on Lepidoptera observed in Hertfordshire during the year 1902. *Trans. Herts. Nat. Hist. Soc.* 12:21–25.

BELL, P. J. (1952) Report on Lepidoptera observed in Hertfordshire in 1948 and 1949, *Trans. Herts, Nat. Hist. Soc.* 23:230–233.

BELL, P. J. (1953) Report on Lepidoptera observed in Hertfordshire in 1950 and 1951. *Trans. Herts. Nat. Hist. Soc.* 24:35–37.

BELL, P. J. (1954) Report on Lepidoptera observed in Hertfordshire in 1952, *Trans. Herts. Nat. Hist. Soc.* 24:72–74.

BELL, P. J. (1955) Report on Lepidoptera observed in Hertfordshire in 1953. *Trans. Herts. Nat. Hist. Soc.* 24:134–135.

BELL, P. J. (1956) Report of Lepidoptera observed in Hertfordshire in 1954. *Trans. Herts. Nat. Hist. Soc.* 24:190–191.

BELL P. J. (1957) Report of Lepidoptera observed in Hertfordshire in 1955. *Trans. Herts. Nat. Hist. Soc.* 24:224–225.

BELL, P. J. (1958) Report of Lepidoptera observed in Hertfordshire in 1956. *Trans. Herts. Nat. Hist. Soc.* 25:27–28.

BELL, P. J. (1959) Report on Lepidoptera observed in Hertfordshire in 1957, *Trans. Herts. Nat. Hist. Soc.* 25:66–67.

BELL, P. J. (1960) Report on Lepidoptera observed in Hertfordshire in 1958. *Trans. Herts. Nat. Hist. Soc.* 25:93.

BELL, P. J. (1961) Report on the Lepidoptera observed in Hertfordshire in 1959. *Trans. Herts. Nat. Hist. Soc.* 25:161–163.

BELL, P. J. (1962) Report on the Lepidoptera observed in Hertfordshire in 1960. *Trans. Herts. Nat. Hist. Soc.* 25:193–194.

BELL, P. J. (1964) Report of the Lepidoptera observed in Hertfordshire in 1961, 1962 and 1963. *Trans. Herts. Nat. Hist. Soc.* 26:31–33.

BELL, P. J. (1966) Report of the Recorder for Lepidoptera for 1964 and 1965. *Trans. Herts. Nat. Hist. Soc.* 26:140–142.

BELL, P. J. (1969) Report on Herts. Macrolepidoptera, 1966–1968. *Trans. Herts. Nat. Hist. Soc.* 27:21–22.

BELL, P. J. (1970) Macrolepidoptera in 1969. *Trans. Herts. Nat. Hist. Soc.* 27:72–73.

BELL, P. J. (1971)Macrolepidoptera in 1970. *Trans. Herts. Nat. Hist. Soc.* 27:108–109.

BELL, P. (1972) Macrolepidoptera in 1971. *Trans. Herts. Nat. Hist. Soc.* 27:207–208.

BELL, P. (1973) Macrolepidoptera in 1972. *Trans. Herts. Nat. Hist. Soc.* 27:229–231.

BELL, P. (1977) Macrolepidoptera of Herts, 1973–1976. *Trans. Herts. Nat. Hist. Soc.* 28:29–33.

BISHOPS STORTFORD NATURAL HISTORY SOCIETY (1950) List of Butterflies. *Trans. Bishops Stortford and District Nat. Hist. Soc.* 1:3–9.

BISHOPS STORTFORD NATURAL HISTORY SOCIETY (1985), *List of Macro-lepidoptera*, Bishops Stortford.

BOWDEN, S. R. (1949) *Lysandra bellargus* and *Thymelicus lineola* in Hertfordshire. *Entomologist*. 82:250.

BOWDEN, S. R. (1963) 'Butterflies and other insects'. In Ross, D. A. (Ed.) *In and around Letchworth*, The Letchworth Naturalists' Society, Letchworth.

BOWYER, R. W. (1888), Some methods of Moth collecting. *Trans. Herts. Nat. Hist. Soc.* 5:23–32.

*Butterflies of Hertfordshire*

BOYD, W. C. (1901) List of the Lepidoptera of Cheshunt and its neighbourhood. *Trans. Herts. Nat. Hist. Soc.* 11:75–86.

BRADLEY, J. D. and FLETCHER, D. S. (1979) *A recorder's log book or label list of British butterflies and moths*, Curwen, London.

BRITISH NATURALISTS' ASSOCIATION (1950–1986) Bulletin of the Hertfordshire and North Middlesex Branch (privately circulated).

CARTER, D. J. (1981) *Butterflies and Moths in Britain and Europe*, Pan, London.

CATT, J. (1978) 'Geology'. In SHIRLEY, D. (Ed.) *Hertfordshire – a guide to the countryside*, Egon Publishers, Letchworth.

COCKAYNE, E. A. (1915) *Agriades corydon*, the Chalk-hill Blue butterfly in Hertfordshire. *Trans. Herts. Nat. Hist. Soc.* 16:81–84 (with plate).

COTTAM, A. (1875) Notes on the observations of Insects in connexion with investigations of seasonal phenomena. *Trans. Watford Nat. Hist. Soc.* 1:50–51.

COTTAM, A. (1900) Notes on Lepidoptera observed in western Hertfordshire in 1897, 1898 and 1899. *Trans. Herts. Nat. Hist. Soc.* 10:185–190.

COTTAM, A. (1902) Notes on the habits of some of our Lepidopterous insects. *Trans. Herts. Nat. Hist. Soc.* 11:222–226.

DONY, J. G. (1967) *The Flora of Hertfordshire*, Hitchin Museum, Hitchin.

DURRANT, J. H. (1885) List of Lepidoptera observed in the neighbourhood of Hitchin and at Knebworth, Herts. *Trans. Herts. Nat. Hist. Soc.* 3:261–266.

DURRANT, J. H. (1888) Contributions to the knowledge of the entomological fauna of Hertfordshire, No. 1 – Lepidoptera. *Trans. Herts. Nat. Hist. Soc.* 5:63–75.

FIRMIN, J. *et al.* (1975) *A guide to the Butterflies and Moths of Essex*, The Essex Naturalists' Trust, Colchester.

FORD, E. B. (1945) *Butterflies*, Collins, London.

FOSTER, A. H. (1916) A list of macrolepidoptera occurring in north Hertfordshire, with notes on each species. *Trans. Herts. Nat. Hist. Soc.* 16:237–258.

FOSTER, A. H. (1934) 'Butterflies and Moths'. In HINE, R. L. (Ed.) *The Natural History of the Hitchin Region*, The Hitchin and District Regional Survey Association, Hitchin.

FOSTER, A. H. (1937) A List of the Lepidoptera of Hertfordshire. *Trans. Herts. Nat. Hist. Soc.* 20:157–279.

FOSTER, A. H. (1940) Hertfordshire Lepidoptera: delenda, addenda and corrigenda. *Trans. Herts. Nat. Hist. Soc.* 21:173–174.

FOSTER, A. H. (1941) Hertfordshire Lepidoptera: further addenda and corrigenda. *Trans. Herts. Nat. Hist. Soc.* 21:272–276.

FOSTER, A. H. (1942) Hertfordshire Lepidoptera: new species and other addenda to the list. *Trans. Herts. Nat. Hist. Soc.* 21:308–310.

FOSTER, A. H. (1944) Addenda to the list of Hertfordshire Lepidoptera. *Trans. Herts. Nat. Hist. Soc.* 22:40–42.

FOSTER, A. H. (1945) Addenda to list of Hertfordshire Lepidoptera V. *Trans. Herts, Nat. Hist. Soc.* 22:84–86.

FOSTER, A. H. (1946) Report on Lepidoptera in Hertfordshire for 1945. *Trans. Herts. Nat. Hist. Soc.* 22:125–129.

FRYER, Sir J. (1948) Report on Lepidoptera observed in Hertfordshire, mostly in 1946. *Trans. Herts. Nat. Hist. Soc.* 23:17–20.

FRYER, Sir J. (1950) Report on Lepidoptera observed in Hertfordshire in 1947. *Trans. Herts. Nat. Hist. Soc.* 23:86–88.

GIBBS, A. E. (1889) Some notes on the Lepidoptera of St. Albans and its neighbourhood. *Trans. Herts. Nat. Hist. Soc.* 5:181–186.

GIBBS, A. E. (1893) Notes on Lepidoptera observed in Hertfordshire. *Trans. Herts. Nat. Hist. Soc.* 7:187–198.

GIBBS, A. E. (1894) Notes on Lepidoptera observed in Hertfordshire during the year 1893. *Trans. Herts. Nat. Hist. Soc.* 8:74–84.

GIBBS, A. E. (1895) Notes on Lepidoptera observed in Hertfordshire during the year 1894. *Trans. Herts. Nat. Hist. Soc.* 8:188–192.

GIBBS, A. E. (1896) Notes on Lepidoptera observed in Hertfordshire during the year 1895. *Trans. Herts. Nat. Hist. Soc.* 9:27–32.

GIBBS, A. E. (1901) Notes on Lepidoptera observed in Hertfordshire in the year 1900. *Trans. Herts. Nat. Hist. Soc.* 11:43–45.

GIBBS, A. E. (1902) 'Lepidoptera'. In PAGE, W. (Ed.), *The Victoria History of the Counties of England: Hertfordshire*, vol 1:110–153, Archibald Constable, London.

GIBBS, A. E. (1902a) Notes on Lepidoptera observed in Hertfordshire in the year 1901. *Trans. Herts. Nat. Hist. Soc.* 11:165–172.

GIBBS, A. E. (1904) Notes on Lepidoptera observed in Hertfordshire in the year 1903. *Trans. Herts. Nat. Hist. Soc.* 12:109–116.

GIBBS, A. E. (1905) Notes on Lepidoptera observed in Hertfordshire in the year 1904. *Trans. Herts. Nat. Hist. Soc.* 12:159–164.

GIBBS, A. E. (1906) Notes on Lepidoptera observed in Hertfordshire in the year 1905. *Trans. Herts. Nat. Hist. Soc.* 13:5–9.

GIBBS, A. E. (1907) Notes on Lepidoptera observed in Hertfordshire in the year 1906. *Trans. Herts. Nat. Hist. Soc.* 13:199–204.

GIBBS, A. E. (1908) Lepidoptera observed in Hertfordshire in the year 1907. *Trans. Herts. Nat. Hist. Soc.* 14:45–48.

GIBBS, A. E. (1911) *Hesperia lineola* in Hertfordshire. *Trans. Herts. Nat. Hist. Soc.* 15:22.

GIBBS, A. E. (1916) The Satyrid butterflies of Hertfordshire: with a short study of *Pararge aegeria*. *Trans. Herts. Nat. Hist. Soc.* 16:173–188 (with plate).

GLADWIN, T. W. and SAGE, B. L. (1986) *The Birds of Hertfordshire*, Castlemead, Ware.

GRIFFITH, A. F. (1884) Notes on the Lepidoptera observed in the neighbourhood of Sandridge, Herts. *Trans. Herts. Nat. Hist. Soc.* 3:58–66.

GRIFFITH, A. F. (1890) Notes on *Tineina* and other Lepidoptera observed in the neighbourhood of Sandridge, Herts. *Trans. Herts. Nat. Hist. Soc.* 6:97–102.

HAILEYBURY AND IMPERIAL COLLEGE NATURAL SCIENCE SOCIETY (1873–1951) Annual Reports.

HAILEYBURY NATURAL SCIENCE SOCIETY (1888) *The Fauna and Flora of Haileybury*, (F. W. HEADLEY, Ed.) Second issue (1902). Third issue (E. D. WAINWRIGHT, Ed.) (1926), Stephen Austin, Hertford.

HALL, M. L. (1981) *Butterfly Research in I. T. E.*, Institute of Terrestrial Ecology, Cambridge.

HEATH, J., POLLARD E. and THOMAS, J. (1984) *Atlas of Butterflies in Britain and Ireland*, Viking, Harmondsworth.

HIGGINS, L. G. and RILEY, N. D. (1980) *A field guide to the Butterflies of Britain and Europe*, Collins, London.

HODGSON, S. B. (1936) Notes on the Lepidoptera of the Berkhamsted district. *Trans. Herts. Nat. Hist. Soc.* 20:41–43.

HODGSON, S. B. (1936a) The Comma butterfly (*Polygonia c-album*) in Hertfordshire. *Trans. Herts. Nat. Hist. Soc.* 20:43–46.

HODGSON, S. B. (1938) The Speckled Wood butterfly (*Pararge aegeria*) in Hertfordshire. *Trans. Herts. Nat. Hist. Soc.* 20:312–313.

HODGSON, S. B. (1939) Macro-lepidoptera in west Hertfordshire. *Trans. Herts. Nat. Hist. Soc.* 21:71–89.

HODGSON, S. B. (1962) Vanishing west Hertfordshire butterflies. *Trans. Herts. Nat. Hist. Soc.* 25:195–196.

HODGSON, L. S. (1939) Notes on the Lepidoptera of the Hatfield district in 1937 and 1938. *Trans. Herts. Nat. Hist. Soc.* 21:69–70.

HOPKINSON, J. (1919), 'Arthur Ernest Gibbs, an appreciation [obituary and list of publications]. *Trans. Herts. Nat. Hist. Soc.* 17:66–73

JACKSON, C. H. (1921) Lepidoptera in Hertfordshire. *Trans. Herts. Nat. Hist. Soc.* 17:291.

JAMES, T. J. (1966) 'Butterflies'. In SAGE, B. L. (Ed.) *Northaw Great Wood: its history and natural history*, Hertfordshire County Council, Education Department, Hertford.

JOINT COMMITTEE FOR THE CONSERVATION OF BRITISH INSECTS, *A code for insect collecting*, JCCBI, Cambridge.

KILLINGBECK, J. (1985) *Creating and maintaining a garden to attract butterflies*, National Association for Higher Environmental Education, Walsall.

KINGSTON, A. (1896) *Royston Heath: its history, its beauty and typical wildflowers*, Warren Bros, Royston.

KITCHIN, V. P. (1905) Notes on variation in *Melitaea aurinia* (*artemis*). *Trans. Herts. Nat. Hist. Soc.* 12:165–167 (with plate).

LAMB, H. H. (1972) *Climate: Present, Past and Future*, vol. 1, Methuen, London.

LEE VALLEY PROJECT GROUP (1974) Annual Report.

LETCHWORTH NATURALISTS' SOCIETY (1941–1957) *Journal*, vols. 1 to 12. Letchworth.

MANLEY, G. (1974) Central England temperatures; monthly means, 1659 to 1973. *Quarterly Journal of the Royal Meteorological Society*. 100:389–405.

MEAD, C. and SMITH, K. (1982) *Hertfordshire Breeding Bird Atlas*, Tring.

MENDEL, H. and Piotrowski, S. H. (1986) *The Butterflies of Suffolk – an atlas and history*, Suffolk Naturalists' Society, Ipswich.

NATURE CONSERVANCY COUNCIL (1982) *The Conservation of Butterflies*, Interpretative Branch, NCC, Shrewsbury.

NATURE CONSERVANCY COUNCIL (1986) *Focus on Nature Conservation No 17. The Management of Chalk Grassland for Butterflies*, Interpretative Branch, NCC, Shrewsbury.

NEWMAN, E. (1874) *An Illustrated Natural History of British Butterflies*, Allen, London.

NEWMAN, L. H. (1967) *Living with Butterflies*, Billing and Sons, London.

NIMMY, E. W. (1921) The occurrence of the Black-veined White butterfly (*Aporia crataegi*) in Hertfordshire. *Trans. Herts. Nat. Hist. Soc.* 17:205–209.

OATES, M. (1985) *Garden Plants for Butterflies*, Masterton, Fareham.

OLDHAM, C. (1921) Bath White butterfly (*Pieris daplidice*) near Watford. *Trans. Herts. Nat. Hist. Soc.* 17:210.

ORMEROD, Miss E. A. (1882) Notes on Insects observed in Hertfordshire during the year 1881. *Trans. Herts. Nat. Hist. Soc.* 2:80–82.

ORMEROD, Miss. E. A. (1883) Notes on Insects observed in Hertfordshire during the year 1882. *Trans. Herts. Nat. Hist. Soc.* 2:187–188.

PENROSE, R. J. (1980) Butterflies and moths at Watford, 1948–1962. *Trans. Herts. Nat. Hist. Soc.* 28:92–100.

PENROSE, R. J. *Butterflies of Whippendell Woods*, Penrose, Watford.

PERKINS, Rev. C. M. (1878) On British Butterflies. *Trans. Watford Nat. Hist. Soc.* 2:63–76.

PETIVER, J. (1702–1709) *Gazophyllacii, Naturae et Artis*, Bateman, London.

PETIVER, J. (1717) *Papilionum Britanniae, Icones, Nomina, etc., Containing the figures, names, places, seasons, etc., of about eighty British Butter-flies, being all that have been hitherto observed in Great Britain*, John Millan, London.

POLLARD, E., HALL, M. L. and BIBBY, T. J. (1976–1985) *Butterfly monitoring scheme*, Institute of Terrestrial Ecology, Monks Wood.

PRATT, C. (1983) A modern review of the demise of *Aporia crategi* L.: The Black-veined White. *Entomologists' Record.* vol. 95:45–52; 161–166; 232–237.

PRATT, C. (1986) A history and investigation into fluctuations of *Polygonia c-album* L.: The Comma Butterfly. *Entomologists' Record.* vol. 98:197–203; 245–250.

RACKHAM, O. (1986) *The History of the British Countryside*, Dent, London.

ROTHSCHILD, M. and FARRELL, C. (1983) *The Butterfly Gardener*, Michael Joseph, London.

RYE MEADS RINGING GROUP (1974), (1987), Report.

SAWFORD, B. (1983) *Wildlife of the Letchworth Area*, Letchworth Naturalists' Society, Letchworth.

SILVESTER, F. W. (1884) Report on Insects observed in Hertfordshire during the year 1883. *Trans. Herts. Nat. Hist. Soc.* 3:91–94.

SILVESTER, F. W. (1885) Report on Insects observed in Hertfordshire during the year 1884. *Trans. Herts. Nat, Hist. Soc.* 3:233–235.

SILVESTER, F. W. (1886) Report on Insects observed in Hertfordshire during the year 1885. *Trans. Herts. Nat. Hist. Soc.* 4:49–52.

SILVESTER, F. W. (1887) Report on Insects observed in Hertfordshire in 1886. *Trans. Herts. Nat. Hist. Soc.* 4:201–204.

SILVESTER, F. W. (1888) Report on Insects observed in Hertfordshire in 1887. *Trans. Herts. Nat. Hist. Soc.* 5:89–92.

SILVESTER, F. W. (1889) Report on Insects observed in Hertfordshire in 1888. *Trans. Herts. Nat. Hist. Soc.* 5:134–138.

SPOONER, G. G. (1963) On causes of the declines of *Maculinea arion* L. (lep. Lycaenidae) in Britain. *Entomologist*, 96.

STEEL, C. and D. (1985) *Butterflies of Berks, Bucks. and Oxon*, Pisces, Oxford.

STEPHENS, J. F. (1828–1834) *Illustrations of British Entomology* (Haustellata). Vol. 1 (1828); Vol. 4 (1834), Baldwin and Cradock, London.

STROYAN, H. L. G. (1950) Range changes in British Butterflies. *Entomologist* 83:210.

STUBBINGS, J. G. (1948) *Danaus plexippus* in Hertfordshire. *Entomologist.* 81:163.

THOMAS, J. A. (1984) The conservation of butterflies in temperate countries: past efforts and lessons for the future. *Symposium of the Royal Entomological Society, London.* No. 11:333–353.

THOMAS, J. A. (1986). *RSNC Guide to Butterflies of the British Isles*, Newnes, Twickenham.

THOMAS J. A., THOMAS, C. D., SIMCOX, D. J. and CLARKE, R. T. (1986) Ecology and declining status of the Silver-spotted Skipper (*Hesperia comma*) in Britain. *The Journal of Applied Ecology.* Vol. 23, No. 2. Aug. 1986, Blackwell, Oxford.

TUTT, J. W. (1896) *British Butterflies*, George Gill, London.

WARREN, M. S. (1984) The biology and status of the Wood White butterfly, *Leptidea sinapis* L. (Lepidoptera: Pieridae) in the British Isles. *Entomologists' Gazette.* 35:207–223.

WATERTON, P. (1979) Lepidoptera report – 1977. *Trans. Herts. Nat. Hist Soc.* 28: Pt. 2:7–8.

WATERTON, P. (1980) Lepidoptera report – 1978. *Trans. Herts. Nat. Hist. Soc.* 28: Pt. 3:7–8.

WATERTON P. (1981) Lepidoptera report – 1979. *Trans. Herts. Nat. Hist. Soc.* 28: Pt. 4:9–10

WATERTON, P. (1982) Lepidoptera report – 1980. *Trans. Herts. Nat. Hist. Soc.* 28: Pt. 6: 33–34.

WATERTON, P. (1983) Lepidoptera report – 1981. *Trans. Herts. Nat. Hist. Soc.* 29: 19–20.

WATERTON, P. (1984) The status and distribution of butterflies in Hertfordshire, 1970–1984. *Trans. Herts. Nat. Hist. Soc.* 29:111–119.

WEST, B. B. (1984) Bedfordshire Butterflies. *Journal of the Bedfordshire Natural History Society and Field Club.* No. 3 – 1948: 16–21.

# Other References

Many sources of unpublished material have been consulted, including collections and manuscripts at the following institutions and organisations

### North Hertfordshire Museums Natural History Department
Lepidoptera collections

Biological Records Centre sites data

Hertfordshire Natural History Society Lepidoptera Recorders' archive of manuscripts and letters

Dr A. H. Foster's manuscripts and letters from correspondents

Letchworth Naturalists' Society archive, including manuscripts of annual entomological reports

Diaries of Ray Palmer: 1922 to 1969 (photocopy of original held by Bedfordshire Natural History Society)

Diaries of S. B. Hodgson of Berkhamsted (extracts): 1930 to 1961 (photocopy of extracts taken from original diaries which are the property of the Hertfordshire Natural History Society)

Diaries of Roger S. Ferry of Welwyn: 1944 to 1946 (photocopy of a copy held at Welwyn-Hatfield Museum)

### City Museum, St Albans
Lepidoptera collections

Biological Records Centre sites data.

### Haileybury College Museum
Lepidoptera collections

Entomolgical card index and manuscripts of the Haileybury Natural Science Society.

### Bishops Stortford College
Lepidoptera collection of Charles Mellows

### Biological Records Centre at Monks Wood, Cambridgeshire
National data files of lepidoptera

### London Natural History Society
Information relating to Hertfordshire supplied by the Recorder for Lepidoptera.

### Buckinghamshire County Records Centre
Data supplied by County Museums Service at Aylesbury.

# Index of Species

English vernacular names appear in roman type, scientific names in italics. The page numbers of individual species accounts are in bold type, and the colour plate reference in italics.

KEY

A  Aldbury Nowers
B  Highdown, Pirton
C  Whippendell Woods/
   Jacotts Hill
D  Knebworth Woods
E  Balls Wood/Hertford Heath
F  Ashridge/Berkhamsted
   Common
G  Hexton/Lilley Hoo
H  Bayfordbury
I  Broxbourne Woods/
   Wormley Wood
J  Hudnall Common/
   Ravensdell Wood
K  Tewin/Bramfield

L  Therfield Heath
M  Bricket Wood
N  Tring Reservoirs
O  Ayot/Brocket
P  Aston/Benington
Q  Radlett
R  Ickleford
S  Hitch Wood
T  Sherrardspark Wood
U  Bulbourne
V  High Scrubs/Tring Park
W  Hook Wood/Potters Bar
X  Weston Hills
Y  Patmore Heath